FLOWER REMEDI

CHRISTINE WILDWOOD is an experienced aromatherapist and Bach Flower practitioner. As well as writing a number of magazine articles on health-related subjects, she is the author of several books, including *Holistic Aromatherapy* and *Creative Aromatherapy*. She lives in South Wales and runs a holistic health practice from her home.

FLOWER REMEDIES FOR WOMEN

Christine Wildwood

Thorsons
An Imprint of HarperCollins*Publishers*

Thorsons
An Imprint of HarperCollins*Publishers*
77–85 Fulham Palace Road
Hammersmith, London W6 8JB
1160 Battery Street
San Francisco, California 94111–1213

Published by Thorsons 1994
10 9 8 7 6 5 4 3 2 1

A catalogue record for this book
is available from the British Library

ISBN 0 7225 2842 6
Phototypeset by Harper Phototypesetters Limited,
Northampton, England
Printed in Great Britain by
HarperCollinsManufacturing Glasgow

CONTENTS

ACKNOWLEDGEMENTS

I am most grateful to Clare Harvey of Middle Piccadilly Natural Healing Centre in Dorset and to Patricia Kaminski of the Flower Essence Society, California, for their warm support of this project and suggestions for the short-list. Thank you also, Patricia, for granting permission to glean information from the Flower Essence Society's excellent *Flower Essence Repertory*, an invaluable source of reference for practitioners and lay persons alike.

Many thanks also to everyone who trustingly 'took the medicine' during the experimental phase of the work, even though they had no idea what the remedies would do for them! And especially to my dear friend Rose, who is always an accurate barometer of the efficacy of the remedies.

And finally, to the memory of Dr Edward Bach, whose genius continues to be an inspiration to many and whose shining spirit lives on through his work.

INTRODUCTION

Although flower remedies, or 'essences' as they are also called, are suitable for people of either sex (and also for animals and even plants), this is one of the few books to look at this system of healing from the female perspective. No doubt ardent feminists will strongly object to the view that women are different from men. Nevertheless, I believe that we are different – not superior, nor inferior, but certainly different. With femaleness comes a unique way of seeing the world which is, at least in part, the product of the nature of our bodies. While male hormones take a relatively smooth course, rising at adolescence, levelling out at maturity and falling at middle-age, female hormones ebb and flow like the lunar tides. This makes women generally more sensitive, yet more buoyant in the currents of change and adversity.

Even in the present era of the 'new man', it is usually the woman who is responsible for caring for other family members in 'sickness and in health'. Moreover, she may also have a job outside the home and yet still be expected to take on most of the domestic chores. 'Well, he doesn't really do it properly' or 'He's had a hard day' are surprisingly common excuses. In truth, society conditions women into feeling guilty if their interests extend beyond the home front. The mythical 'perfect wife and mother' still looms large in the minds of many women.

Conversely, we must not forget the woman who has chosen to stay at home with her children, but is made to feel guilty as a result of media pressure and the remarks of career-minded friends who tell her she is 'vegetating' at home and should be out in the world. When her role as wife and mother is grossly undervalued in this way, of course she begins to suffer from low self-esteem.

Not surprisingly, then, surveys from doctors' surgeries reveal that women are particularly prone to 'stress' in its many guises, especially fatigue. On the positive side, because women are possessed of an innate wisdom, they are more open to the idea of alternative and complementary therapies. Indeed, statistics show that women buy more books on such subjects and are more likely to become practitioners themselves. Moreover, because women are also possessed of a basic openness to change and growth, they are more likely to respond well to subtle methods of healing, especially to flower essences – as many practitioners will testify.

Those already familiar with flower therapy will know that the remedies are prescribed according to the distressing emotions of the sufferer rather than the physical symptoms of illness – problems such as anxiety, lack of confidence, depression and apathy. How then can we gear this system of healing towards the state of being female, when negative states of mind are universal by nature, transcending both gender and species?

While it is true that we as individuals, whether male or female, respond in our own unique way to the everyday pressures of life – and, indeed, to the physical and emotional changes associated with the transitions of puberty, parenthood, middle-age, bereavement and eventually to the experience of our passing – it is also true that there is a range of feelings common to many at such times. It may be adolescent moodiness, the over-protective parent syndrome, the 'mid-life crisis', the sorrow of bereavement or a deeply held fear of dying. But unlike a man, a woman has the potential for experiencing several other rites of passage during her lifetime: the onset of menstruation, pregnancy, childbirth and the menopause. While many women sail through these phases with the minimum of physical and emotional discomfort, others can be extremely distressed by them.

Even if you do not experience the physical symptoms commonly associated with certain phases of the female life-cycle, it would be a rare woman indeed who could fail to be stirred emotionally, mentally and spiritually by such profound change. The intensity and quality of each transition, be it joyful, interesting, beset by a few minor problems or utterly wretched, varies from woman to woman, depending on several interrelated factors. Much depends on our physical health, which needs to be maintained by sensible nutrition, fresh air, sunlight, adequate exercise and sound sleep. Heredity also plays a part (most unfairly it seems), for some people are born healthier than others. Moreover, if your mother and grandmother experienced a relatively smooth passage through each phase of womanhood, chances are that you will too.

Much also depends on our attitude, which is partly determined by upbringing, but this can be changed if we so wish. Do you regard menstruation, for instance, as 'the curse', or as a magical time of enhanced creativity? Do you dread the onset of the menopause as if it were somehow the beginning of a downward spiral of mental and physical deterioration, or do you see it as an initiation into the Wise Woman aspect of your being? How we relate on a deep level to our femininity will almost certainly affect our experience of the body's natural processes.

We need also to nurture the spiritual aspect of 'self', for we are more than a body and a mind. The spiritual aspect is hard to define, but is tied up with our relationship with ourselves, with other people and with our sense of purpose and meaning – and, some would say, with the health of our planet.

In the last decade, there has been a growing acceptance of scientist James Lovelock's Gaia hypothesis (a name from Greek mythology for the goddess of Earth). In this theory, the Earth is far more than a mass of rock and water hurtling through space; it is an infinitely complex, living, evolving entity, constantly striving for balance – an organic system of which we ourselves are a part. (Incidentally, this realization has been embraced by mystics and philosophers for thousands of years.) Tragically, our planet is under the most severe strain. Deserts are advancing; rainforests are being destroyed at an alarming rate; water, soil and air are being degraded and polluted. Like ourselves, Gaia can adapt to potentially harmful changes, but she can only do this within narrow limits. Should those limits be surpassed, she dies. Quite a sobering thought.

But all is not lost. We need to envision a future where such qualities of compassion, intuition and nurturing – qualities which are part and parcel of the philosophy of the truly holistic healer and the Green movement in general – have become integral to human consciousness as a whole. In so doing, we will once again begin to honour the Earth, as did the ancient healers, farmers and mystics, realizing that we and Gaia move together in the one Dance of Life.

However, putting intuition back into medicine (and using flower essences is a step in this direction) does not mean we have to go completely overboard into the realms of Earth magic at the total expense of the orthodox approach. There needs to be a marriage between the two seemingly opposing principles of Yin and Yang (the Chinese term for the archetypal Feminine and Masculine, which can be expressed as intuition and logic respectively). In other words, we need to integrate science with mysticism, and the best of orthodox medicine with the best of the gentler approaches, for logic is dehumanized without the balance of intuition and feeling. And as most physicians, therapists and carers would agree, Tender Loving Care is the most potent healing force of all.

With the present upsurge of interest in anything that could be remotely categorized as 'spiritual', 'Green' or 'New Age', the flower essences certainly resonate in harmony with the mood of the times. While it is also true that flower therapy is still regarded as somewhat 'fringe', even by certain holistic practitioners, its value as a tool for self-knowledge or 'personal growth' is rapidly gaining ground. Moreover, there is a growing number of orthodox medical practitioners, particularly in the United States, employing flower essences to augment conventional treatments. The flower essences help to alleviate the emotional and psychological stresses many patients experience, thus hastening the healing process.

The beauty of the flower essences is that they are usually collected from the wild or organically grown in gardens – that is to say, without the use of artificial fertilizers and poisonous sprays. In addition, preparation of the remedies neither damages nor destroys the remedy plants, for only the flowers are used, shortly before they are about to fall. Moreover, the remedies are benign in their action, both non-toxic and non-addictive, and can be taken by people of all ages – including pregnant women, babies and young children. This is because the remedies represent plant energy rather than the bio-chemical properties of the plants from which they are prepared, a phenomenon which I have attempted to explain in Chapter 2.

As touched upon earlier, flower therapy is not an alternative to orthodox treatment, nor indeed an alternative to any other system of healing. It is best described as *complementary* to other approaches. The flower essences address the emotional, mental and spiritual aspects of our being. Therefore, they do not interfere with any other means of healing the body – indeed, most progressive physicians and therapists working with the essences would agree that they enhance other forms of treatment. The remedies engender optimism, thus enabling us to become better able to deal with the ups and downs of life. However, the remedies do not encourage the blind optimism of emotional immaturity. As always, we need to aim for a balanced perspective. The purpose of the remedies is to bring out the best in us, to help us develop our strengths and wisdom. Bach encouraged the development of our individuality, which can become stifled by the pressures of society and the demands of 'significant others'.

The most difficult task in preparing this book was in deciding which flower essences to include, for there are so many. The most commonly known are the 38 *Bach Flower Remedies*, which were developed by the visionary physician

Dr Edward Bach (pron. 'batch'), who discovered – some would say 'rediscovered' – this approach to healing in the late 1920s.

As a matter of interest, the ancient Chinese used a similar system of healing as referred to in the Tao. The earliest record of the use of flower essences in Europe occurred in the sixteenth century, when the great healer and mystic Paracelsus collected dew from flowers to heal emotional disharmony. Since the 1960s, other flower essences have continued to be developed by various people.

My own experience as an aromatherapist and flower remedy practitioner is largely confined to the Bach Flower Remedies, which I employ to broaden the psychotherapeutic action of aromatherapy treatments. However, I have also been experimenting with other flower essences, particularly those developed in California and the Australian bush.

In order to round out the picture, in researching this book I have interviewed a number of other therapists employing the more recently developed flower essences as an adjunct to their work. Unfortunately, space would not afford a full description of every essence within each of the flower therapy systems mentioned. So with the help of Clare Harvey, a British practitioner and teacher of flower therapy, and the suggestions of Patricia Kaminski, co-director of the Flower Essence Society in California, I have selected those essences which I believe would be most helpful to women (and also to their children). However, the entire Bach Flower Remedy pharmacopoeia is covered, partly because I am most familiar with these remedies, but also because being the best known of the flower essences, they are the ones most often sold in health shops. Other flower essences are obtainable by mail order (see addresses on pages 124–5).

Instructions for other supportive measures, such as nature attunement, dreamwork, gentle stretching exercises, deep relaxation and so forth, are included in order to encourage a full and active participation in our own healing – a very important tenet of holistic therapy which seeks to create balance within the whole *bodymind* complex.

In Chapter 5, I have chosen to equate the female life-cycle to the seasons: spring, summer, autumn and winter. In so doing, I do not wish to offend the woman who may not have become a mother during the summertime of her life, or the woman who has chosen to have a baby at the beginning of autumn, nor indeed the woman who will never become a mother (for whatever reason), or the one whose life has been shortened by terminal illness. Of course no woman's life is as neatly ordered as suggested here, so please allow for poetic licence! Above all, this book is as much a celebration of being female as it is about healing.

Christine Wildwood,
Spring Equinox, 1993

Chapter One

THE DEVELOPMENT
OF FLOWER THERAPY

The Bach Flower Remedies

It was during the summer of 1991 that I first climbed the tread-worn steps to Mount Vernon, an unpretentious little house set in the heart of the Oxfordshire countryside. The simple beauty of the red brick house with its free-spirit garden perfectly mirrors its earlier resident, the late Dr Edward Bach, founder of the Bach Flower Remedies. The 38 Remedies which comprise the Bach pharmacopoeia have been prepared at Mount Vernon for nearly 60 years. Indeed, the present trustees of the work, John Ramsell, his daughter Judy Howard and their helpers, continue to collect wild flowers from the same locations and use the original methods of preparation as devised by Bach in the late 1920s and early 1930s.

Upon entering Dr Bach's consulting room, which continues to be used as such today, I was struck by its stillness, enhanced by the simplicity of the heavy wooden furniture which Edward Bach built with his own hands. A glass medicine cabinet houses a number of intriguing looking corked bottles filled with some of Bach's original flower tinctures which he prepared many years ago. According to John Ramsell, these remedies are still potent. On rare occasions, and with what can only be described as a kind of 'religious relic reverence', a drop or two of a precious tincture may be used to boost a flower remedy prescription for a particularly needy person.

A photograph of the doctor takes pride of place on the mantelpiece, a rather solemn portrait depicting a youngish man with large dark eyes reflecting a spaniel sadness. Yet by all accounts, though unconventional (some might say Bohemian) and often volatile, he was a lovable person with a wonderful sense of humour and a kind heart. He would give everything away, not only his services free of charge to the poor (he practised medicine in the era prior to the advent of the British National Health Service), but also the shirt off his back if he thought that someone else was in greater need. Seeing the smile return to the faces of those who had suffered was his greatest joy.

Edward Bach's father, who owned a brass factory in Birmingham, had expected his son to take a prominent place in the family business, but on learning of Edward's true vocation readily provided the means for him to enter Birmingham University in 1906. He continued his studies at University College Hospital, London, where he qualified in 1912. In 1914, he received the Diploma of Public Health from Cambridge.

Being a free-thinker, Bach spent more time on the close study of the patients themselves, rather than their particular maladies. He came to realize that continual stress resulting from emotions such as anger, fear or worry lowered a person's resistance to disease. The body would then become prey to all manner of infection or illness, whether it be a cold, shingles, a digestive upset or something much more serious. At the same time, he discovered that a person's emotional outlook influenced the course, severity and duration of their illness. He also noticed that people suffering from the same disease and sharing similar personalities responded well to a particular remedy, but that others of a different temperament needed other treatment, although suffering from the same complaint. Thus Bach's axiom became: 'Take no notice of the disease, think only of the personality of the one in distress' (an almost unheard of principle in conventional medicine at the time). In this view, he was sharing the opinion of Plato as well as that of many contemporary practitioners of holistic medicine.

Bach was himself an example of his own doctrine. In July 1917 he was diagnosed as suffering from advanced cancer and given three months to live. Overwork, lack of sleep and emotional turmoil were contributing factors, for he had been torn by the death of his first wife and his love for the woman he then married soon afterwards. However, much to everyone's amazement, he pulled through – a triumph of his own powers of mind over matter, fuelled by an all-embracing need to fulfil his life's mission.

In 1919, having taken a position as pathologist and bacteriologist at the London Homoeopathic Hospital, he was enthralled to discover the work of a kindred spirit, Samuel Hahnemann, the founder of homoeopathy, whose axiom was: 'Treat the patient and not the disease.' Hahnemann realized that the idea that disease is a material factor, curable only by material agents, is a fallacy. He paid great attention to the psychological aspects of illness.

The basic law of homoeopathy is that 'like cures like'. In practice, this means the treatment of disease by infinitesimal doses of drugs that in a healthy person would produce the physical and emotional symptoms of the disease. Or, more simply, that any substance that can make you ill can also cure you if given in a tiny enough dose. With the exception of vaccination (which is a like treating like approach), orthodox medicine is based on the premise that disease can only be treated with drugs having the opposite effects to the symptoms.

Bach's homoeopathic studies opened the doors of his perception to the reality of vibrational healing. He was aware that highly diluted medicinal substances, so diluted that not a single molecule of the original material can be detected in the laboratory, are capable of triggering a powerful healing effect in the body. This knowledge was to influence the development of the seven *Bach Nosodes* (remedies homoeopathically prepared from substances of pathological origin) which are still used to this day in homoepathic medicine, and eventually to the development of his own system of healing.

By 1922, Bach's work at the London Homoeopathic Hospital had increased so much that he had little time for his own researches. While working at the hospital, he also held down a busy practice in Harley Street as well as a surgery in Nottingham Place, where he treated the poor free of charge. Indeed, his growing fame brought him almost more work than he could cope with. However, there was still a great deal of work to be done with the seven nosodes and his research into intestinal toxaemia in its relation to cancer. So he gave up his hospital post and moved into a large laboratory in Portland Place.

After several years of research and much acclaim, both from the homoeopathic and the orthodox medical establishment, he was still dissatisfied. It had ever been his wish to replace the products of disease (the intestinal bacteria used as vaccines) by purer remedies, and he determined that his future researches should be to that end.

THE KEY

The inner harmony and freedom of spirit that Bach experienced whenever he was close to nature persuaded him that the key to true healing lay not in the laboratory, but among the plants, trees and herbs of the field.

Furthermore, his instincts told him that poisonous substances of animal, plant or mineral origin should play no part in healing, even when used in infinitesimal doses as in homoeopathy. He felt that there was something beyond traditional homoeopathy, that the healing of body, mind and spirit occurred not by repelling disease with the darkness of substances of a similarly low vibration, but as a result of flooding our being with the light of a higher vibration 'in the presence of which, disease melts away as snow in the sunshine'.

His quest, therefore, was to find the plants that were capable of restoring the peace of mind and happiness which he believed to be the essential nature of our being. It is this essence, or the Higher Self as some would call it, that is aware of our true mission in life and endeavours to realize this through the mind and emotions: the personality. However, the personality is not always aware of the Higher Self, so we often fail to hear the promptings of our inner voice. We go through life only half awake, guided by social conditioning and our subjective responses to the life experience. As a result, according to Bach, instead of experiencing joyfulness, purposefulness, wisdom and courage, we experience disharmony. If we could act wholly in harmony with our own spirit or Higher Self (which itself is part of the greater whole, embracing the rest of humanity and, as illustrated by the Gaia hypothesis mentioned earlier, Mother Earth), we would fulfil our potential and experience profound happiness. Where there is a disconnection between the Higher Self and the personality, there is dis-ease.

Obeying his own intuition, in the early autumn of 1928 Bach travelled to Crickhowell in South Wales where, by the river Usk, he was inspired to gather the blooms of the wild Mimulus and Impatiens. He felt that these flowers, if made into homoeopathic medicines, would prove beneficial to certain of his patients. His preliminary findings proved promising. However, he was not entirely happy with the time-consuming process of homoeopathic potentization, which entailed a series of dilutions, over a number of days, of the 'Mother Tincture' (a preparation of the medicinal material suspended in alcohol) alternated with 'succussion' – vigorous shaking. He was to eventually develop a simpler method which could be employed by most people, not just the skilled practitioner. Above all, he was seeking a method of healing which would be accessible to everyone – an approach calling for no medical training, simply a natural sensitivity and feeling for others.

Incidentally, I am fortunate enough to live just a few miles from the very spot where Edward Bach first discovered the aforementioned flowers. Although much of the marshy ground has been drained for agricultural purposes, both plants still grow abundantly by the river. During the summer and early autumn, the gloriously yellow Mimulus and the delicate pinky-mauve Impatiens are a joy to behold.

Unfortunately Bach's second marriage crumbled. The reason for this (and most other details concerning Bach's private life) have been kept under wraps. Through a sense of loyalty to his memory, those 'in the know' are unwilling to disclose any information on the subject.

Early in 1930 Bach was suddenly inspired (for there is no

other word for it) to give up his lucrative London practice to seek new plants for his developing system of healing. Within a fortnight, he had divided his extensive practice amongst his medical friends and closed down the laboratory. Much to their dismay, he burned all his research papers and smashed all his syringes and vaccine bottles, pouring the contents down the sink. Then he persuaded his trusted friend and colleague Nora Weeks (formerly a radiologist at his Harley Street practice) to accompany him on a journey through Wales and the south east of England, a fascinating journey that was to last several years.

Immediately after leaving London, they settled down in a village near Bestws-y-Coed in North Wales. Living close to his beloved nature, Bach's innate sensitivity blossomed fully. He was already aware of his gift of healing, for many times he had suddenly felt the impulse to lay his hand on a patient's arm or shoulder and that person would feel a rush of healing energy flooding their body. Whilst in Wales, his sensitivity became so highly developed that he had merely to place a petal on his tongue or hold his hand over a flowering plant to be aware of its effects upon the mind, body and spirit.

As his sensitivity developed, Bach was to gain his knowledge of plants in a different and rather alarming way: for some days before the discovery of a healing flower he experienced in himself, in a magnified form, the distressing state of mind for which that particular flower was a remedy. He suffered intensely in his quest, both physically and mentally. Indeed, such sensitivity, combined with self-neglect through over-work, cigarette smoking and an inherently weak constitution (he was never a robust child) was to shorten his life.

On the beach at Abersoch in North Wales, Bach dictated to Nora Weeks the concise yet profound work entitled *Heal*

Thyself (first published in 1930), a booklet which was to become a classic in the field of flower therapy. In this work, Bach proclaims that certain flowers are of a 'Higher Order' and hold a greater power than those ordinary medicinal plants which heal the body on a biochemical level. The true healing plants address disharmony within the mental and spiritual spheres. They transmute negative emotions such as fear, melancholy and hatred into courage, joy and love; and in this manner, according to Bach, they correct the *cause* of our ills. But, unlike powerful mind-bending drugs, they do not simply buffer the effects of a turbulent perception; they act as a gentle catalyst, bringing to the fore that which is already a positive aspect of our nature. In Bach's own words: 'The human being becomes very much himself again at a point where he had ceased to be quite himself.'

Just how the flower remedies achieve this, no one really knows for certain, though the answer may partially lie in 'field theory', a relatively new school of scientific thought which has grown since the 1920s (see Chapter 2).

A SIMPLE METHOD OF POTENTIZATION
Whilst living in Wales and communing with nature, Bach first stumbled upon the idea that the early morning dew must absorb some of the properties of the plant upon which it rested. He decided to test this theory by collecting dew from certain plants and trying it out on himself. Through his finely developed senses, he found that the dew held a definite power of some kind. Moreover, the dew collected from plants exposed to sunlight was far more potent than that collected from plants growing in the shade. He also found that the essential energies of a plant were concentrated in the flower rather than in any other part such as the roots or leaves.

Having proved to himself that sun-warmed dew absorbed the properties of the flower upon which it rested, Bach set himself the task of finding a simple method for capturing the flower energies (collecting dew proved to be too time-consuming). He also sought a method which would neither destroy nor damage the plant itself and, at the same time, could be carried out by anyone capable of identifying the specific wild flowers. In fact, he was to devise two methods of extraction, or 'potentization', as he preferred to call it: the Sun Method and the Boiling Method.

In the Sun Method, the best flower heads are carefully picked. These are put into a thin, clear glass or crystal bowl filled with spring water and float on the top. The bowl is then placed on the ground (near the parent plants) where it is exposed to strong sunlight for a few hours, until the healing energy of the blooms is transferred to the water. Afterwards, the flowers are carefully removed with a twig or leaf from the remedy plant, thus avoiding human contact with the vitalized water or 'essence'. The essence is then poured into bottles half-filled with brandy, which acts as a preservative. (Incidentally, flower essences should not be confused with the aromatic essential oils of plants which are captured by distillation, and which are also known as 'essences'. Except for the brandy preservative, flower remedies are odourless.)

A few years later, as his work developed, Bach realized that certain blooms of plants and trees, such as Star of Bethlehem, Willow and Elm, required a different method of extraction, though he did not explain why. It was for these flowers that he devised the Boiling Method.

In this process, plant material (buds, cones, or flowers) is placed in an enamel pan of spring water and simmered for half an hour. Afterwards, the pan is covered and left to cool.

When cold, the essence is filtered and, as in the previous method, preserved in equal quantities of brandy and labelled 'Mother Tincture'.

The next stage in the preparation, whether using the Sun or the Boiling Method, is to dilute the Mother Tincture in a further quantity of brandy. This bottle is labelled 'Stock Concentrate', and it is in this form that the remedies are usually sold. Although the stock is a dilution of the original tincture, it is nevertheless considered to be a concentrated remedy because it requires further dilution in spring water before administration (see Chapter 3).

Two of the Remedies in the Bach flower repertory are a little different, for they are not prepared from European wild flowers. These are *Rock Water* (potentized spring water) and *Cerato*, a cultivated plant native to the Himalayas.

THE FINAL YEARS

Over the years, Edward Bach and Nora Weeks spent much time in Cromer on the Norfolk coast where they lived in a little house overlooking the sea, and from where Bach successfully treated many patients with the newly found remedies. In 1934, they finally moved to the Thames Valley. It was not long before Mount Vernon, in the village of Sotwell, became their home. Little did they know at the time that their humble home was to become known as The Bach Centre, attracting visitors from all over the world. It was from Mount Vernon that Bach perfected his work, with the help of Nora and two other friends, Victor Bullen and Mary Tabor, and it was from here that he quietly departed in his sleep in the winter of 1936, satisfied in the knowledge that his mission on Earth had been accomplished.

Further Discoveries

Shortly before his death, Bach declared his work complete. The 38 Remedies, he believed, addressed every negative state of mind known to humanity. However, there are many who would dispute this claim. For instance, the Bach Remedies do not appear to address such areas as sexuality, communication and creativity. Moreover, it would be ludicrous to suggest that there are no other flowers of a 'Higher Order' to be found growing outside Europe. Indeed, as mentioned earlier, even Bach made an exception of the Himalayan *Cerato*.

Four decades after Bach, American researcher and 'growth psychologist' Richard Katz began to develop essences from flowers native to northern California, using his intuitive faculties and the Bach Sun Method of potentization. Following the success and popularity of the Californian essences, in 1979 he founded the non-profit making Flower Essence Society. FES is now a world-wide organization of professional health practitioners and interested laypersons who are devoted to the development and application of flower therapy. As well as conducting training courses and seminars throughout the world, FES promotes clinical and empirical research into the therapeutic effects of flower essences.

More recently, naturopath Ian White has developed the Australian Bush essences, a few of which are profiled in Chapter 4. He says the Aborigines have always known of many flowers that can be used for resolving specific emotional imbalances.

Since the 1960s flower essences have continued to be developed by a number of individuals, not only in Britain, the United States and Australia, but also in the Amazonian rain forests, Alaska, Hawaii, the Himalayas and other wild and beautiful places throughout the world. The healing flowers are revealed through various intuitive methods, the most common being contemplation of the plant whilst in a relaxed or meditative state, dowsing and *channelling* (the New Age term for mediumship whereby guidance is sought from spirit beings). However, at risk of upsetting the proverbial apple cart, I have to admit my own reservations regarding channelled information, preferring instead to attribute such wisdom to the Higher Self. There is a tendency, even in esoteric circles, to greatly underestimate the breadth of the human psyche.

In addition to the aforementioned methods of discovery, many flower essence researchers abide by the ancient cross-cultural Doctrine of Signatures. According to folklore, plants have been signed by their Creator with visible clues to their usefulness. Employing the 'like cures like' principle, yellow plants such as dandelion and celandine, for example, would be effective against jaundice. The skullcap flower resembles the shape of the human skull, thus it has been used as a remedy for headaches and insomnia. The spotted leaves of the herb commonly known as lungwort suggested to the ancient herbalists the appearance of diseased lung tissue, therefore it was used for diseases of the upper respiratory tract. As a matter of interest, the efficacy of the Doctrine of Signatures has been verified by modern herbalists, who continue to use the above plants for the same ailments. Moreover, the biochemical constituents of the plants would indicate their usefulness in the conditions for which they have been used for centuries.

The Doctrine of Signatures is also applicable to flower therapy. The drooping, languid appearance of the branches of the *Larch* tree, for instance, mirrors the mental state for which the Bach Remedy is indicated – lack of confidence and despondency. In the FES repertory, *Trumpet Vine* is the remedy for those who need to be clearly understood, the public speaker for example. The *Grey Spider Flower*, whose essence is included in the Australian Bush repertory, is most interesting. The rusty brown flower is covered with a fuzz of greyish white hairs, with the extremely long tendril-like pistils forming the 'spider's legs'. According to Ian White, if you look into this flower you can clearly see a face, with two sunken eyes and a wide-open mouth! Needless to say, this is the remedy for terror, fear of the supernatural and of psychic attack. Perhaps it could also help those who have a morbid fear of spiders?

HUMAN POTENTIAL

It would seem appropriate at this point to justify the use of intuition in the seeking of flower essences. Contrary to popular belief, the human being is a potentially super-sensitive creature. It was not merely by chance – or, even more crudely, by a game of Russian roulette – that our ancestors singled out the edible and healing plants from those that were poisonous. They were almost certainly endowed with highly developed sensory and intuitive powers seen only in the few remaining native tribes alive today.

In his eminently readable series of books written in the early 1960s, anthropologist Colin Turnbull cites many examples of tribal peoples' sixth sense. For example, one night whilst living with the Pygmies, the author was apprehensive about going to bed – for good reason. A great tree, which had suffered in the previous night's storm, looked as if it were about to fall on his hut. However, his Pygmy friend with whom he shared the hut assured him the tree would not fall for many hours, nor would it cause any damage. So Turnbull reluctantly lay on his bed, listening to the alarming creaking of branches while his friend slept soundly. In the early hours of the following morning, however, the tribesman suddenly awoke, yelling at Turnbull to get out of the hut fast! Within a few seconds the tree fell, missing the dwelling by inches.

There are also well documented reports of Native American hunters who are able to follow prey for long distances by using their senses, particularly the sense of smell. They can even distinguish the scent of other human beings by sniffing the ground where they may have walked.

We have not entirely lost this animal ability to use our senses for survival. It has merely been a case of conditioning and adaptability. In his book *Body Power*, Dr Vernon Coleman cites the case of an American prisoner who had developed considerable hunting skills. He was able to identify warders by their scent, breathing patterns and the sound of creaking joints as they walked. He could even smell (sense?) a packet of cigarettes hidden in a coat pocket 30 yards away!

Yet, for the most part, we in the Western world are slaves to our scientific instruments and to our intellect, having lost the freedom to experience through finely tuned senses. Ideally, we need to merge the two sides of our psyche: the logical aspect with the under-used intuitive part. Without such an effort, we may on the one hand experience life through a distorted haze, without any common or shared basis of reality, or on the other, by shutting ourselves off from our basic instincts, become impoverished of spirit, little more than a humanoid functioning on only one cylinder.

Let us continue our exploration by delving more deeply into the flower essences' mode of action.

Chapter Two

HOW DO FLOWER ESSENCES WORK?

Mind Over Matter

Before we can begin to understand how flower essences work, we need to move away from the philosophy of materialism, which asserts that only matter is real. Materialists argue that the body (and indeed all life) is essentially biochemical in nature, and that human consciousness is merely a function of matter. But can we really reduce the human being to the level of chemicals?

We tend to view the body as a machine composed of many parts and functions operating in separate compartments, when in fact, like the Earth's eco-systems, everything is invisibly linked. At any one time we breathe, eat, talk, think, digest our food, fight off infection, renew our cells and much more besides. Blood cells, for example, rush to the site of a wound and begin to form a clot. These cells have not travelled there by chance; they are animated by a seemingly intelligent force. They 'know' where to go and what to do when they arrive. In the words of Dr Deepak Chopra, author of *Quantum Healing*: 'Intelligence makes the difference between a house designed by an architect and a pile of bricks.' Or to put it another way: at death, the chemicals are still present, but something has gone.

Just what is this 'something'? Although we may never know the absolute truth, modern science has begun to move closer towards understanding the nature of the 'life-force'.

In the 1970s, a new class of minute chemicals called neuro-transmitters and neuro-peptides was discovered. A revolutionary discovery as it turned out, for these brain chemicals appeared to fill the gap that apparently separates mind and body.

Amazing as it may seem, neuro-chemicals cannot exist without the animating power of thought. To put it another way, they are actually *created* by thought! 'To think,' says Chopra, 'is to practice brain chemistry, promoting a cascade of responses throughout the body.' Moreover, receptors for neuro-chemicals are to be found in other parts of the body such as the skin and on cells in the immune system called monocytes. These 'intelligent' blood cells circulate freely throughout the body, apparently sending and receiving messages just as diverse as those in the central nervous system. This means that if, when we are happy, depressed, angry, in love or whatever, we produce brain chemicals in various parts of the body, then those parts also must be happy, depressed, angry or in love. Moreover (as if this were not astonishing enough), insulin, a hormone always associated with the pancreas, is now known to be produced in the brain as well, just as brain chemicals such as transferon and CCK are produced in the stomach. Without doubt, the interrelated *bodymind* is a reality.

However, this does not explain the origin of thought. Could it be that mind energy is an interrelated aspect of an even greater vibration, which we might call the Universal Mind?

Scientists such as astronomer Sir Arthur Eddington have

suggested that an intelligent force holds the universe together: 'The stuff of the world is mind stuff.' More recently, theorists such as British physicist David Bohm have reached a similar conclusion: that there is an 'invisible field' holding all of reality together, a field that possesses the property of knowing what is happening everywhere at once. This is the quantum mechanical world, a world beyond the atom, the proton, electron and quark – all of which can be broken down into smaller particles (at least in theory) and therefore occupy space. Whatever it is that shapes the universe and bestows it with life is non-material – it takes up no space. Rather, as quantum physics has shown, it is composed of energetic activity within a unified field.

At the quantum level, all forms of existence, from a human being to a crystal, are essentially the same, that is to say, energy or vibration. Moreover, it appears that the animating force that shapes the potential development of all things is also capable of change or expansion – just like the human mind. The eminent biologist and researcher Rupert Sheldrake has accorded this concept the term 'morphic resonance'. It is a phenomenon which is testable by experiment.

As scientists will verify, new compounds are generally difficult to crystallize, sometimes taking weeks or even months to form, yet as time goes on, they tend to form more readily. This is because when a newly synthesized or organic chemical is crystallized for the first time – say, a new drug – there will be no morphic resonance or 'memory' from previous crystals of this type. Therefore, a new morphic field has come into existence. The next time the substance is crystallized – anywhere in the world – morphic resonance from the first crystals will speed up subsequent processes of crystallization. A cumulative memory, which does not fall off by distance, will build up as the pattern becomes more habitual.

Similarly, the phenomenon can be observed in the animal kingdom. You may have heard of the 'hundredth monkey syndrome'. One enterprising monkey from a particular species decided to go down to the river to rinse some earth-caked roots before eating them. Within a few months, all monkeys in the area had adopted this new behaviour. Furthermore, a morphic pattern had been established, for within a short period monkeys of the same species hundreds of miles away were also washing the earth off edible roots! It was observed that it takes about one hundred members of a species to adopt a new behaviour for it to become generalized within the species as a whole.

Morphic resonance also occurs in the sphere of human ideas; though many attribute the phenomenon to the better known Collective Unconscious – the term coined by the eminent psychologist and mystic Carl Jung. For example, Picasso and Braque, independently of one another, both hit upon the idea of the Cubist style of painting, while the scientists Watt, Cavendish and Lavoisier simultaneously discovered the composition of water. Moreover, Charles Darwin was not the only one to formulate the theory of evolution: the British naturalist Alfred Wallace made parallel investigations at about the same time.

Vibrational Healing

We might say we perceive ourselves as separate from other things because different manifestations of nature vibrate at different frequencies. Mind energy, for instance, vibrates so fast that it appears to be invisible, whereas rock vibrates so slowly that we are unaware of its essential dynamism. Likewise, humans are 'deaf' to high and low frequency sounds, but, as every physicist knows, this does not mean we cannot be affected by them.

The flower essences, then, are in tune with the finer frequencies of the mind/spirit. In fact, there are many other healing methods which act on a subtle or vibrational level: for example, homoeopathy, spiritual healing, colour therapy, music therapy, crystal healing and gem elixirs. The latter are similar liquid preparations to the flower essences, using the energy of precious and semi-precious stones to heal or balance the emotional, mental and spiritual aspects of our being.

In order that we may glean further insight into the efficacy of vibrational healing, let us return to the world of science. Although the following account concerns itself with the principles of homoeopathy, it is also relevant to the mode of action of the flower essences in that infinitesimal quantities are used.

In 1987, a French immunobiologist shook the foundations of the non-quantum medical establishment – which by and large is still bound by the Newtonian mechanical physics of the seventeenth century – when he proved that certain highly diluted substances could be as potent as vastly greater quantities of the same substance. In laboratory tests, Dr Jacques Benveniste demonstrated that living cells could be influenced by Immunoglobulin E in dilutions so high that it was unlikely that a single molecule remained in the test solution. Rather, only the energy pattern or 'memory' of the original medicinal material could have triggered the effect.

Despite the fact that Benveniste's discovery defied the laws of materialism, he duplicated the experiment 70 times, and asked other scientists to repeat it in Israel, Canada and Italy. All came up with the same result.

Even though Benveniste's findings were published in the June 1988 edition of the prestigious British journal *Nature*, the editors frankly declared their disbelief. Much to their chagrin, Benveniste was lending credence to the methods of homoeopathy, which, as already mentioned, employs minute amounts of antagonistic substances to heal the body. Still in the throes of 'belief system shock', shortly after publishing the results of the experiment, *Nature* sent a team of experts to France to view Benveniste's findings. Unfortunately, he was unable consistently to duplicate his results: some trials worked, others did not. So *Nature* condemned Benveniste's work, calling his results a 'delusion', and ignoring the fact that the original paper had been signed by 12 other researchers in four countries. Moreover, they failed to comment on the experiments which did work.

In view of what we have already discovered about the nature of mind, is it possible that the negative vibes emanating from the sceptical observers could actually have hampered the trials?

The Human Energy Field or Aura

Many therapists working with flower essences believe that the healing effect is triggered in the human energy field, or aura, which surrounds and interpenetrates the physical aspect. From this field, which is essentially a thought form, the healing effect of the essences filters 'inwards', as it were, eventually triggering a response at the physical level. In contrast, material medicines such as herbs and drugs move 'outwards' from the physical level, eventually affecting the aura.

This is actually an over-simplification because, as we have seen, there is no true separation of the bodymind. All matter and energy is a manifestation of the same thing, distinguished by velocity of vibration. So it is just as important to care for the body on the denser physical level by means of a healthy diet and lifestyle, with the occasional help of herbal remedies, massage, conventional treatments and so forth, as it is to nurture the mind/spirit aspect. For without an holistic approach to health and healing, there is an imbalance of energies. However, this is not to undermine the ultimate superiority of the mind/spirit – some people fail to respond to treatment despite doing everything 'right'.

Although psychics describe the aura differently, according to their own level of perception, it is generally agreed that the aura is a vibrating energy field of a rainbow hue (some psychics can see its colours) surrounding and interpenetrating the body. It reflects our thoughts and feelings as well as our state of health. The energy radiates at least three feet around the physical form, and is composed of several 'layers' of energy, each layer vibrating at a different frequency. The part of the subtle body closest to the physical level, emanating about an inch from the body, is the *etheric* field. This is very interesting because it vibrates at a frequency which can be detected by a high voltage technique called Kirlian photography. The information captured by this process shows a kind of luminescence and steams of energy flowing from the hands or feet. To the trained eye, these patterns reflect the emotional and physical state of the individual and can be used as a diagnostic tool.

As a matter of interest, a number of doctors and nurses in the USA have been employing an auric healing technique known as Therapeutic Touch, a term which was coined by Dr Dolores Krieger in the 1970s. The technique, based on the methods employed by spiritual healers, has been refined and its effects documented by many practitioners. It is based on the fundamental assumption that there is a universal life energy that sustains all living things, a concept which can be linked to the field theory mentioned earlier.

In Therapeutic Touch, which is used to complement conventional treatments, this vital energy is channelled into healing through relaxed yet focused intent on the part of the therapist. Sweeping movements of the hands a few inches from the recipient's body are used to pick up the congestions, deficits and imbalances. Disharmony within the field may be perceived by the therapist as uncomfortable tingling, for instance, or excessive heat, coolness and, where there is serious imbalance, perhaps over the site of a diseased organ, a total depletion of energy. Obstructions are cleared through the power of thought, the therapist serving as a conduit for a universal force. Energy is thus replenished and harmony is restored.

Therapeutic Touch has been found particularly helpful for people suffering from wounds, burns and infections, post-operative shock, anxiety and stress. While not a miracle cure, the method has been shown to uplift the recipient's spirits, thus alleviating physical discomfort and generally hastening the healing process.

Experiences in Flower Therapy

Similarly, the flower essences – more often the Bach Flower Remedies because they are better known – are used by enlightened physicians to help uplift the spirits of hospital patients, thus contributing to their healing. In his book *Flowers to the Rescue*, George Vlamis includes the testimonials of numerous orthodox practitioners, from all over the world, who use the Bach *Rescue Remedy* (see page 56) to complement other treatment. Indeed, most evidence and case studies on flower essences are subjective and anecdotal, people reporting positive changes in attitude, insight and enhanced well-being.

Bach, in tune with many other mystics, believed that the

purpose of disease is to hinder and prevent us from carrying our negative thinking too far:

> It is a lesson to teach us to correct our ways and to harmonise our lives with the dictates of our soul . . . When the lesson of pain and suffering and distress is learnt, there is no further purpose in its presence, and it automatically disappears.
> From *The Original Writings of Edward Bach*, J. Howard and J. Ramsell (C. W. Daniel, 1990).

But does it? Even the most ardent supporter of the 'mind over matter' stance would concede that, although the emotional state may be altered, the physical, pathological changes may have gone too far to follow suit. However, as Nora Weeks would remark of those who took the Bach Flower Remedies prior to passing on, 'Well, they at least died happy!' And to die happy is to be *truly* healed!

Surely though, some disorders are purely physical in origin – food poisoning, malaria, typhoid and so on? The answer must be 'yes' *and* 'no', depending on one's perspective. We might say that disease can stem from the visual world and filter through to the more subtle aspects of our being, at least to the emotional and mental levels. However, according to esoteric philosophy (which mirrors Bach's own beliefs), life on Earth is a schooling. The immortal spiritual aspect has chosen to learn through suffering and setback, even through congenital defect, mental illness and poverty. So in this respect, the true origin of illness and suffering (even accidents) is spiritual. Life was never meant to be easy – and that is the hardest lesson of all to learn (and one which I myself do not pretend to fully understand, nor even to accept graciously!) Unfortunately, it is beyond the scope of this book to go deeply into the philosophy of esoteric healing, so I urge the enquiring reader to obtain a copy of Edward Bach's *Heal Thyself*.

Undoubtedly, the flower remedies in Bach's own hands proved most efficacious – indeed, miraculous on occasions. However, we need to consider how much of this can be attributed to Bach's own extraordinary gift of healing (many times he healed the seriously ill by the 'laying-on of hands'), and how much to the flower remedies themselves. It is my own belief that while the remedies are efficacious in their own right, they may also become imbued with the vibrations of the therapist. Indeed, many flower remedy practitioners (and also their clients) use positive affirmation or prayer to boost flower remedy prescriptions.

Incidentally, I have seen Kirlian photographs of the energy field of a piece of wholemeal bread, before and after being touched by a healer. The photographs show the ability of the healer to positively influence the energy field of the bread, whose radiance is significantly increased. Similarly, it is feasible that the practice of blessing food or saying grace before meals improves the quality of the food by raising its vibrations. Conversely, it could also be argued that the energies of certain individuals may act to diminish the vibratory quality of substances – as indicated by the Benveniste experiments mentioned earlier.

In my own experience, which is mirrored by many other therapists of different schools of healing who were interviewed, flower therapy cannot totally negate the need for any other form of treatment, especially in serious or chronic illness. Nevertheless, the remedies (by this I mean all flower essences, not just the Bach Remedies) are extremely supportive, and on occasions can be sufficient in themselves, as I trust you will soon discover.

Chapter Three

HOW TO USE FLOWER ESSENCES

The Art of Prescribing

Whether you are choosing remedies for yourself or for another person, the key to successful prescribing lies in the ability to identify specific obstacles or issues to be overcome. On first acquaintance with the flower essence repertory, many people feel that at least a dozen remedies are indicated, or that they need all of them! However, it is important to refine the process of selection, choosing preferably no more than four flowers to be taken at a time, and certainly no more than six. Some practitioners are of the opinion that too many remedies in a mixture can lead to a decreased sense of well-being as a result of too much stimulation or too many issues being stirred up at once.

As a matter of fact, Bach made a point of testing a composite of his 38 remedies. Although he did not record any negative effects as such, he was not entirely satisfied with the result. He found the vibration of a single carefully chosen remedy had a deeper and more profound effect than that of several. However, he also realized that many people may temporarily require a mixture of flowers.

In order to prescribe successfully for others, you will need to have a caring, perceptive nature combined with a broad experience of life. It is also important to develop the ability to look at another person unblinkered by your own hang-ups, life experiences, social conditioning, religious and political persuasion, and prejudices. Very few people actually reach such a non-judgmental state of being, but we can at least try. We can begin by becoming conscious of our own stumbling blocks, conditioning and areas of restricted growth. Talking things through with an understanding person who can empathize with us is a necessary part of the growth process and will help us connect with our own inner strengths.

If you intend eventually to set yourself up as a flower remedy practitioner, it would be of enormous benefit to broaden your knowledge by gaining some counselling skills and a recognized counselling qualification. Although not an easy ride (trainees are normally expected to undergo counselling themselves), this would be a great step forward in the quest for greater understanding. Do find out about courses in your area.

Prescribing for yourself can sometimes be more difficult than prescribing for others for it takes a great deal of self-knowledge. Moreover, you may not find it easy to be objective about yourself when your spirits are low. So it may be best to ask a friend, partner or close relative to help you choose the correct remedy or combination of remedies. But be prepared for a few home truths!

Getting Started

The best way to begin using the essences is to write down the remedies you feel would be most helpful. Refer to the repertory in the following chapter and any relevant information in Chapter 5, which deals with specific issues and transitions from the female perspective. If there are too many remedies on your list, look at each one more closely in order to ascertain the most pressing areas of imbalance. Cross off those remedies which you feel could be helpful at a later date, or perhaps dispensed with altogether. This is an important exercise in itself, enabling one to focus on key issues and to begin opening to the possibility of change.

TYPE REMEDIES

You will discover that some of the Bach Remedies correspond to one's basic 'type', or character, as a whole. For example, you may be an extrovert, a natural leader and very outspoken. This would suggest remedies such as *Vine*, *Vervain* and *Impatiens*. If, on the other hand, you are quiet and reserved, then look to remedies such as *Centaury*, *Mimulus* or *Water Violet*. Each remedy has its positive as well as its negative aspect. The positive side to the *Vervain* personality, for example, is seen in one who realizes that others have the right to their opinions and has the wisdom to change their mind as a result of argument and debate. However, when the *Vervain* personality moves out of kelter, the negative aspect comes to the fore: emotional and physical strain as a result of over-enthusiasm; a driving need to convert others to their own way of thinking. Remedies that address the personality in this way will be needed at intervals over the course of a lifetime.

HELPER REMEDIES

The 'helper' remedies address the superficial emotional states that are not characteristic, but temporary. For instance, you may harbour feelings of jealousy or hatred towards a former partner's new lover (*Holly*), or feel nervous and apprehensive about visiting the dentist (*Mimulus*).

In practice, most flower essences can be used as either a type remedy or a helper remedy. For example, *Honeysuckle* is the type remedy for the person who prefers to live in the past. Such a person may become despondent every Hogmanay, mourning for the fading year. It could be said that Nostalgia is the name of their soul! Yet the same remedy can help the person who is normally optimistic about the future, but who may have moved home or changed their job and now regrets the action, dwelling on how much they miss their old life. Or there is the *Scleranthus* type who can never make up their mind. The remedy also helps those who suffer fluctuating moods, perhaps at the menopause or during the pre-menstrual phase, irrespective of type.

Many of the new flower essences are similar to homoeopathic remedies, for in addition to their effect on the emotions they are known to help certain physical conditions. The Bush Remedy *She Oak*, for example, appears to balance female hormones, therefore it is an excellent remedy for pre-menstrual syndrome, as is the Californian essence *Pomegranate*. When choosing remedies to help a named physical condition (see Chapter 6), try to include at least one other essence which corresponds to the individual's personality or emotional state at the time.

ACCENTUATE THE POSITIVE

When prescribing for another person, it is important to encourage them to dwell on the positive virtues to be achieved (see the 'Positive Potential' note included with each remedy profile in the following chapter). For instance, instead of emphasizing that *Vine* is for someone's bossy, overbearing nature, let them go away with the knowledge that *Vine* will help them develop the qualities of a wise and compassionate leader or teacher who inspires others. Instead of calling the *Gentian* type a 'doubting Thomas', help them to develop the certainty that their problems can be overcome.

Needless to say, dwelling on the positive is also important when prescribing for yourself.

Subtle Diagnostic Techniques

DOWSING AND MUSCLE TESTING

The most helpful flower essences can be determined by certain subtle or psychic techniques such as dowsing and muscle testing. In muscle testing, the subject is asked to stand erect with their right arm raised to a horizontal position. With their right hand, the tester pushes gently down for two seconds, with the palm open, on the subject's extended arm, to feel the normal muscle strength. Then the subject holds a flower essence bottle in their left hand. The tester then reassesses the subject's muscle power by gently pressing down on the raised arm. If the flower essence registers as positive, the subject's arm will stay up. However, if a flower essence is unsuitable the arm may shake or give way under the slightest pressure. In other words, the most beneficial flowers will strengthen the muscle, or will have no effect, while those of no value at the time of the test will weaken the muscle.

Incidentally, just because a remedy appears to weaken a muscle, this does not mean it is 'poisonous' to the individual concerned. We might say that the subject's Higher Self assesses whether or not a remedy is appropriate for their needs at the time. The Higher Self then communicates its decision through the bodymind, answering 'yes' or 'no' in its own way.

Muscle testing (and dowsing) can also be employed to discover hidden food allergies. In this instance, however, a negative response may well indicate that a particular food is unhealthy for that person. Many eczema sufferers, for example, find their skin improves if they cut out dairy products such as cow's milk and cheese. Yet another person may thrive on these foods.

With dowsing, the prescription can be determined by swinging a pendulum over each of the remedies to be tested (preferably with the bottles' labels out of view so as not to influence the outcome through auto-suggestion). The tester asks, silently or aloud, whether the remedy being tested is appropriate. If testing for another person (in their absence) some dowsers place the test bottle near a 'witness', that is to say, a lock of hair or some nail clippings donated by the subject. The pattern of the pendulum's swing determines the outcome. Most dowsers (though not all) regard a clockwise swing as positive, which means that the remedy is indicated, and an anti-clockwise movement as negative. Sometimes the pendulum will swing from side to side, indicating a neutral response. This could mean that the remedy may be required at a later date.

While subtle methods of diagnosis can be remarkably accurate – in the right hands! – they should not be relied upon at the expense of the more mundane approach discussed earlier. If you are an adept dowser (this takes a great deal of practice), by all means use this skill to broaden the possibilities of flower therapy. But it is enough to have a thorough knowledge of the remedies spiced with a little intuition and a basic understanding of human nature. With practice, it will soon become fairly easy to perceive the 'atmosphere' of a person and to prescribe accordingly.

DREAMWORK

A few years ago I discovered a simple method of dreamwork,

a creative practice which has proved to be an invaluable tool for the imaginative flower essence practitioner. It is also a method which can be employed in self-diagnosis and, when you have gained experience, in the diagnosis of others.

Most dreams represent situations and patterns needing resolution and, contrary to what you may believe, they do not generally provide answers to our problems (though they have been known to do so). Instead, they pose questions and invite responses. Therefore, rather than getting bogged down in dream symbolism and interpretation, which can be very misleading to the beginner, concentrate on the feelings and responses, or lack of response, your dreams evoke in you, and prescribe accordingly. For example, you may be shocked by an expression of jealousy and violence in a dream (*Holly*), or by some other equally powerful reaction rarely expressed in the non-dreaming state, for what we do not deal with in life will come up in our dreams. Recurring dreams are particularly significant in this respect. Likewise, the inability to sleep, or to remember our dreams, is sometimes due to a resistance to processing repressed material requiring expression.

If your dream reactions are similar to those in your outer life, then this indicates that you have already achieved a certain amount of self-awareness. If they are very different, however, then this suggests there is much repressed emotion to be dealt with. Interestingly, those who lead rather miserable or monotonous lives are apt to have wonderful dreams in vivid colour – as a form of compensation no doubt!

Flower essences tend to activate the dream life, which is why it is useful to keep a record of your dreams for about a month whilst taking the remedies. Once you can identify recurring themes and emotions, you will be in a good position to begin deeper work with the remedies. In fact, you can even ask for a significant dream just before falling asleep; the unconscious will usually oblige. Indeed, it is a well known phenomenon in psychotherapy that where there is a genuine desire for growth, whatever dreamwork method is adopted – be it Jungian, Freudian, Gestalt or perhaps the simple method suggested here – the client will dream to suit. Moreover, they need not fully understand the theory. It appears that the unconscious, or the Higher Self, is an all-knowing entity forever striving to enlighten the relatively naïve conscious mind by whatever means it can muster, even if it means communicating through a mediator – that is to say, via the therapist and their chosen frame of reference!

Keep a pen and notebook beside the bed, and immediately on waking (for dreams fade very quickly) write down all you can remember about a significant dream (there is no need to record every dream). Any dream that triggers a definite emotion might be significant, especially if it is an emotion rarely expressed in the non-dreaming state. If the memory of a dream does evade you, record the particular emotion or mood it evoked. Then try to answer the following questions, which are based on the work of dream therapist Strephon Kaplan-Williams. Do not be concerned if you cannot answer every question fully; simply deal with as many issues as you can. The purpose of the exercise is to enable you to view your dreams from the flower essence perspective.

1. What am I doing and why am I doing it?
2. What do I most need to deal with in this dream?
3. Would I react this way in life or am I reacting in a very different way?
4. What in this dream is related to things in other dreams I have had?

5. What in this dream is related to what is going on in me or in my life at present?
6. Why did I have this dream? What do I need to look at or make a choice about?

The purpose of writing is to externalize or make more concrete that which hitherto has had the advantage of being able to work in the dark of the unconscious. It is by viewing a disturbing feeling, memory or image in the sunlight of conscious awareness that it becomes less threatening, perhaps totally disempowered. However, should your dreams be overwhelming, perhaps stemming from some half-forgotten childhood trauma, it would be advisable to seek the aid of an accredited counsellor or therapist who will help you work through the feelings, thus enabling you to release them.

Consider the following dream recorded by Jane, a recently divorced woman in her early thirties. She had chosen to work with the remedies because she had been feeling generally low for some time, but could not pin-point the reason for her sadness. She was in a happy relationship, her partner being a kind and attentive man. Her job as a shop assistant in a busy bookshop she described as 'reasonably interesting'. On the surface, she appeared calm and well-balanced. For several weeks, she recorded in her diary a series of rather bland, unemotional dreams – usually a re-hash of the day's events. We appeared to be making little progress. However, as is common in dreamwork, just as we were about to try a different approach, the breakthrough came:

I find myself looking through the French windows of my ex-husband John's house. A blazing coal fire burns in the ornate fireplace. His beautiful girlfriend Sue brushes her long blonde hair, admiring herself in the mirror that hangs over the mantelpiece. John walks towards me, smiling. He opens the window and invites me in. He tells me he's just bought two tickets for a weekend in Paris, a surprise for Sue. I feel overwhelmed with grief and resentment. I scream out, 'She's more attractive to you than I'll ever be! You never gave me such expensive presents!' I wake myself up crying, 'It's so unfair!' I'm left feeling ashamed and guilty for having been so childish.

Although a psychoanalyst would read a great deal into the symbolism of this dream, in flower therapy the most important aspects of the dream are the dreamer's feelings and actions or *reactions*. The flower remedies will do the rest – that is to say, they will trigger the process of healing by addressing the feelings of bitterness, resentment and shame, which incidentally Jane had never openly expressed because she had not been consciously aware of harbouring such feelings. It had been she who had initiated divorce proceedings (having met someone else), not her ex-husband, whom she believed still loved her. The flower essences chosen in this instance were *Willow* for her 'poor me' attitude and her depression, *Pretty Face* for her jealousy and shame, and *Pine* for her guilt.

At the time of writing, Jane is still working with the remedies and dealing with the issues highlighted in her dream. She feels that dreamwork has helped her focus on the underlying cause of her unhappiness, thus enabling her to take a great step forward in her quest for self-knowledge.

Responses to Treatment

People vary enormously in their response to treatment, depending upon individual sensitivity and the degree of openness to change. While some report dramatic insights and an enhanced sense of well-being, it is more usual to become aware of subtle changes over a period of weeks or months, to feel gradually more optimistic and better able to deal with the ups and downs of life.

During the first weeks of treatment, the flower radiations may only embrace the superficial emotions rather than the deep-rooted fears and conflicts which are causing the present physical or mental condition. However, by dealing with each new emotional state as it arises, earlier blockages will eventually work through to the surface and out of your system. When this happens, you might notice a temporary worsening of physical symptoms and experience lesser or greater crises of consciousness. Any aggravation will only last a few days and should be taken as a positive sign that the correct remedy has been chosen. It is often said that 'you cannot get out what is not already there', so such a reaction is not a side effect, as in drug therapy, but an indication that your own bodymind is correcting itself, the flower essences acting as a catalyst in the process.

However, should you feel overwhelmed by the changes taking place in your body and mind (though this is an extremely rare occurrence), you should discontinue use of the flower essences and seek professional help from a flower remedy practitioner or counsellor well-versed in the area of 'personal growth'.

How to Administer Flower Essences

Flower remedies come in little dropper bottles of 'stock concentrate', and because of the brandy preservative, they have an indefinite shelf-life. Although the drops can be taken undiluted straight from the dispensing bottle, the usual method is to dilute the remedy in a quantity of spring water before administration. Once diluted, however, the mixture will keep for no longer than three to four weeks.

PREPARATION OF THE TREATMENT
The standard dilution is two drops from each chosen bottle of stock (but no more than six different flowers at a time) to a 30 ml dropper medicine bottle (obtainable from most chemists) three-quarters filled with spring water or mineral water. The bottle is then topped up with some brandy or cider vinegar, which acts as a preservative. Alternatively, leave out the preservative, fill the bottle with spring water and store in the fridge. Tap water can be used instead, though it does tend to turn stale sooner than bottled water, unless boiled and allowed to cool before use. If a 30 ml dropper bottle is difficult to obtain, a slightly smaller or larger bottle will suffice.

A 30 ml treatment bottle will be enough for a three or four weeks' course.

Important: With the Bach *Rescue Remedy*, a composite of five flowers, the quantity is doubled to four drops, whether taken diluted or neat. Moreover, when combined with other flowers, *Rescue Remedy* is considered to be one remedy.

DOSAGE
The standard dosage is four drops of the diluted remedy on the tongue three to four times daily. Some practitioners recommend that the bottle be shaken each time before use to activate the remedy. If using a single flower, you could take the remedy neat, two drops at a time. However, when taking a mixture, it is far easier to dilute the remedies as described earlier.

The most beneficial times for taking the remedy are upon rising and at bedtime. So if you forget to take an afternoon dose, it should not make that much difference, unless you are in an acute state of distress, in which case the remedy can be taken as often as required until you feel better. If preferred, the stock concentrate can be diluted in a small glass or cup of spring water, fruit juice or herb tea.

Important: The Australian Bush essences are reckoned to be a little stronger than most other essences, so for sensitive individuals, the morning and bedtime dose should be sufficient. This still holds true even when the Bush essences are mixed with other flower remedies such as the Bach and Californian. However, if you feel you need more than two doses a day, prepare two treatment bottles, one containing only the Bush prescription, and the other the Bach, Californian or whatever other essences you may have chosen to work with.

It is most helpful to hold the dose in your mouth for a few seconds before swallowing and to visualize the flower vibrations flooding your whole being. It is also helpful to think about why you are taking the essences and to picture in your mind the desired outcome.

PREGNANCY, BABIES AND NURSING MOTHERS

Flower essences, particularly the Bach Remedies, are perfectly safe and highly beneficial for the expectant mother and her unborn child. The method and treatment is no different from usual. Moreover, the remedies can be given to newborn babies (as well as older children). These special uses are discussed in Chapter 5, which offers advice on prescribing for infants – even though they are unable to tell us about their state of mind.

The number of drops used for infant dosage (and for older

children) is the same as for adults. Four drops of the diluted remedy (without the additional brandy or cider vinegar preservative) are added to the baby's bottle or taken in a teaspoonful of boiled water or fruit juice three to four times a day.

Nursing mothers can take the diluted remedies themselves. The flower vibrations will then be imparted to the baby through the mother's milk. Alternatively, moisten the baby's lips with the diluted remedy.

EXTERNAL TREATMENT

Flower essences can be incorporated into massage oils, creams and ointments or added to the bath. Although insoluble in fatty substances (due to the brandy preservative), the quantity required is so tiny that any separation of oil and flower essence is hardly noticeable. Exact quantities are unimportant, for we are dealing with plant energy rather than anything measurable. However, the following suggestions should serve as a guide.

Massage Oils
Add two to four drops of each chosen stock concentrate to a 100 ml bottle of massage oil.

Baths
Many flower essence users put the remedies in the bath to augment oral doses. Add five drops of each chosen stock concentrate to the bathwater or a teaspoonful of the diluted mixture.

Creams and Ointments
Rescue Remedy is a wonderful addition to any antiseptic ointment, skin salve or lotion. With the handle of a teaspoon, stir in four drops to every 30 g or cream or

ointment. Add three drops to every 25 ml of lotion and shake well.

I remember reading somewhere that the negative emotion of regret accelerates the ageing process of the skin. So why not make a 'No Regrets' skin cream, lotion or tonic? A few drops of *Honeysuckle* or, perhaps even more appropriately, *Pretty Face* mixed into a beauty preparation should work wonders!

DURATION OF TREATMENT

There are no hard and fast rules about the length of time the remedies should be continued. Treatment is always geared to individual needs. For acute conditions such as the effects of bad news (*Rescue Remedy* or *Star of Bethlehem*), that 'Monday morning feeling' (*Hornbeam*) or fearfulness before an interview (*Mimulus*), for example, take the drops as often as needed. This could be every 15 minutes or so until you feel better. Most people experience some relief almost immediately.

When dealing with deeply ingrained negativity – a domineering and inflexible personality, for example, or the lingering effects of childhood abuse or trauma – the healing process may take many months. As each layer within the psyche begins to peel away like the many layers of an onion, different emotions will emerge, feelings we may have held in check for many years. Make a note of any negative change (of course, positive feelings will also come to the fore) and change the prescription accordingly. Or, if you have been working with only one or two essences, a new remedy can be added to the existing treatment bottle.

An indication of improvement is when we begin to feel better both physically and emotionally and when our family and friends notice the difference – but more especially when we forget to take the remedies! This means we are becoming

less self-interested and beginning to flow outwards to others
and the world about us.

Using the Bach *Rescue Remedy*

The Bach *Rescue Remedy* is a composite of five flowers. It is the
remedy for all for emergency situations – where there is
panic, shock, hysteria, mental numbness, even unconsciousness. Where there is unconsciousness, the neat or diluted
remedy can be applied externally. Moisten the lips, gums,
temples, back of the neck, wrists or behind the ears.
Although the remedy cannot replace medical attention, it can
alleviate much distress whilst the person awaits the arrival of
medical aid, thus enabling the bodymind's healing processes
to commence without delay.

Bach advised that we should carry a small bottle of *Rescue
Remedy* with us at all times. It is also a good idea to keep a
bottle in the bathroom cabinet or in the first-aid box.

The five flowers which comprise the *Rescue Remedy* are:

- *Star of Bethlehem:* for shock and numbness;
- *Rock Rose:* for terror and panic;
- *Impatiens:* for great agitation, irritability, and tension;
- *Cherry Plum:* for violent outbursts and hysteria;
- *Clematis:* for the bemused, faraway sensation that
  often precedes a faint and for unconsciousness.

Radiation Remedies

We live in a world subject to ever increasing levels of radiation
which emanates from high voltage power lines, radio,
television, computer screens and so on. It is believed that
radiation in its many guises may be responsible for a wide
range of illness, from fatigue, nervous tension, headache and
insomnia to muscular sclerosis and certain forms of cancer.

Moreover, some research has also suggested that the prolonged use of VDUs can cause miscarriage or, even more alarmingly, birth defects. Other research, however, offers conflicting evidence. (This is almost certainly due to the idiosyncratic nature of our response to all forms of stress and pollution.) A study of 4,000 pregnant women recently conducted at the University of Michigan showed that those who work at VDUs for less than 20 hours per week do not increase their risk of miscarriage (birth defects were not mentioned), but that full-time workers show a slight increase in the number of miscarriages. In view of the risks, no matter how slight, it might be wise to give up the VDU for some time before starting a family.

Fortunately, however, most of us are able to adapt to a certain degree of radiation, including that which in some people causes 'geographic stress' – the effects on the bodymind of natural radiation coming up from underground streams or from granite.

Even so, in response to growing concern about radiation, British physician Dr Aubrey Westlake, President of the Psionic Medical Society (England), has developed the *Radiation Remedy*. This formula is believed to help alleviate the effects on the human energy field of all forms of radiation, be it nuclear fall-out, X-rays, microwaves, radiation therapy for cancer, VDU screens and so on. The remedy consists of a mixture of the following Bach Flowers: *Cherry Plum*, *Star of Bethlehem*, *Rock Rose*, *Gentian*, *Vine*, *Walnut* and *Wild Oat*.

PREPARATION

Add approximately three grams of sea salt to a bottle containing 100 ml of spring water; then add two drops of each flower remedy. Shake the bottle well. The dosage is four drops three or four times a day. If you spend many hours each day in front of a VDU screen or a colour television, for example, you will need to take the remedy for an indefinite period.

Incidentally, you may also find the cactus *Cereus peruvianus* helpful. This species, commonly called Column Cactus, is known to absorb radiation. It has been said that the cactus's growth rate will accelerate if placed on top of a computer or television set! At the time of writing I have been unable to obtain a specimen, so cannot confirm this.

As another point of interest, researchers such as British scientist Dr Mike Adams have discovered the radiation-blocking powers of clear quartz crystals. A large crystal, say 7–10 cm long and about 4 cm wide, can be placed close to the mains fuse-box. This acts to prevent power socket radiation (which can sap the vitality of certain sensitive individuals) from going beyond that point. Similarly, small quartz crystals can be placed on and around televisions, microwave ovens and computer terminals to help 'fight back' the radiation.

Yet it is possible to become addicted to radiation. Dr Adams warns that during the first week of using crystals as an anti-radiation measure, some people suffer a worsening of emotional and physical symptoms – though he assures us that withdrawal symptoms are temporary and harmless, and may be alleviated by whisky or champagne! (He also suggests *Rescue Remedy*.)

The remedy I find most helpful for VDU stress – which manifests as a sore neck, eyestrain, irritability and headache – is the Californian *Yarrow Special Formula*, which presents the flower essence in a sea salt solution. The remedy was formulated by Richard Katz in 1986 in response to the Chernobyl nuclear disaster. The dosage is the same as for *Rescue Remedy*.

To compensate for the tension that may be caused by working at a VDU, it is important to take breaks every hour or so. Get up, walk around or do simple stretching exercises. If you are physically able, and if circumstances allow, the yoga Salute to the Sun sequence is a wonderful revitalizer (see pages 116–18).

As a final word on the subject of VDU stress, according to research carried out by the American Food and Drugs Administration, often it is not the computer that causes problems, but environmental factors such as poor lighting or seating, and perhaps increased worker tension because of heightened workload. People who are satisfied with their jobs are less likely to suffer from VDU-related symptoms. So we return to the mind over matter phenomenon!

Chapter Four

FLOWER ESSENCE PROFILES

Flower Therapy Systems

There is a growing number of flower therapy systems and consequently a bewildering array of essences to choose from. Indeed, there now seems to be a remedy to brush away the cobwebs from every conceivable nook and cranny of the human psyche. The psyche must be as vast as the Cosmos! However, for the purpose of this book, I have chosen to feature just three systems: the Bach Flower Remedies, the Californian essences and the Australian Bush essences. For reasons of space and simplicity, the profiles are brief. The Bach Flower repertory is outlined in its entirety. From the other two repertories, I have selected several popular essences, including those recommended by therapists for embracing certain states of disharmony commonly associated with the female life-cycle.

Most experts in the field of flower therapy are of the opinion that the more recently developed flower essences, especially the Australian Bush essences, are stronger than the Bach Remedies. Therefore, unless specifically recommended here, they should not be taken during pregnancy nor given to babies and young children without first seeking the advice of an experienced flower remedy practitioner. Should you wish to delve deeper into flower therapy, see the Suggested Reading list on page 123.

The Bach Flower Remedies
Guide to the Bach Repertory

For each of the Bach Flower remedies listed below, details are given of a *Pattern of Imbalance* and *Positive Potential*. A person does not have to display every personality trait or emotion listed under the Pattern of Imbalance in order for a particular flower essence to be indicated. Common sense combined with a thorough knowledge of the remedies and a measure of intuition will help you refine the process of selection.

The Positive Potential is, of course, the ultimate transmutation whereby the positive aspects within the psyche are brought to the fore, freed from the chains of fear, doubt, anger and uncertainty. It would be unrealistic, however, to suggest that the flower remedies alone can bring about such a remarkable change in every case, especially if the condition is very deep-rooted. Therefore, it is important when treating yourself or others to recognize your own or the other person's limitations and to seek professional help where necessary, in the form of counselling, psychotherapy or even a physical therapy such as massage, herbal medicine or orthodox treatment. As we have seen, the remedies work in harmony with other treatments, hastening the process of healing.

For children – though essentially a child is no different from an adult of a similar disposition – a note is included at the end of each profile to help elucidate and to round out the picture. For guidelines on infant diagnosis, see page 97.

AGRIMONY
Agrimonia eupatoria

Pattern of Imbalance: Mental torture concealed behind a happy-go-lucky façade; fears being alone; anxious; avoids arguments; rarely complains; weak-willed on occasions; desires excitement; even when seriously ill, plays down problems and jokes with nursing staff; restless; addictive behaviour to mask problems; suicidal tendencies.

Positive Potential: The ability *truly* to laugh at life because personal problems are viewed from a more balanced perspective–that of the genuine optimist who possesses an innate talent for creating harmony where there is discord.

The Child: Appears outwardly cheerful but, as the mother or closest carer knows, suffers inwardly. Great importance is attached to the impression they are making on their friends, family and teachers.

ASPEN
Populus tremula

Pattern of Imbalance: Inexplicable fears stemming from the psyche; nightmares; fear of some impending evil; delusions; suicidal tendencies; ungrounded; may be psychic.

Positive Potential: Fearlessness in the knowledge that one's Guardian is the universal power of love.

The Child: Such children suffer from recurring nightmares and may even sleepwalk; they very often demand that a light be left on all night.

BEECH
Fagus sylvatica

Pattern of Imbalance: Intolerant, hypercritical and arrogant; lacks empathy and therefore has few friends; has high ideals; irritable; rigid in mind and body; perfectionist expectations of others – even the small habits, gestures and mannerisms of others are annoying, the degree of displeasure bearing no relation to the cause.

Positive Potential: Tolerance and understanding of the difficulties of others; the ability to see the good in everyone and everything.

The Child: May be reflecting parental attitudes (consider this deeply), or is perhaps feeling belittled by an elder, more dominant or popular sibling.

CENTAURY
Centaurium erythraea

Pattern of Imbalance: Lacks will-power to refuse the demands of others, therefore becomes a 'doormat'; suppresses own needs to keep the peace and to gain favour in the eyes of another; overly conventional; sapped by others; over-sensitive; may be mediumistic.

Positive Potential: To know when to give and when to withhold; the ability to mix with others while preserving one's own identity; to live life according to one's own true mission.

The Child: Quiet, sensitive and responsive – hardly any trouble, but may be prey for the school bully.

CERATO
Ceratostigma willmottiana

Pattern of Imbalance: Annoys others by constantly asking their advice; may imitate others, their style of dress and even their mannerisms; appears foolish at times; saps others; lacks concentration; is easily dominated.

Positive Potential: Trusts own inner voice; gains self-confidence, highly developed intuition.

The Child: This state of mind is more likely to emerge during adolescence. The young person constantly seeks the approval of their peers, perhaps by insisting on wearing the most fashionable clothes, whether they suit them or not! It may be wise to let them grow out of this phase in their own good time (a valuable learning experience).

CHERRY PLUM
Prunus ceraisfera

Pattern of Imbalance: Fear of losing grip on sanity; uncontrolled outbreaks of temper; suicidal tendencies; fear of harming self or others; nervous breakdown; violent temperament through fear.

Positive Potential: Balance and equanimity despite extreme anguish, for the distress is healed by the harmonious forces of the Higher Self.

The Child: Sudden uncontrolled outbreaks of rage, especially when such children throw themselves on the ground or hit their head against the wall – the typical temper tantrum.

CHESTNUT BUD
Aesculus hippocastanum

Pattern of Imbalance: Failure to learn by experience; that 'Oh no, not again!' feeling; lacks observation; a slow learner; thoughts often in the future.

Positive Potential: The ability to keep the attention in the present; to gain knowledge and wisdom from every experience.

The Child: Finds it difficult to pay attention; a slow learner. In spite of being reminded, will keep forgetting a lunchbox or pencil case, for instance.

CHICORY
Cichorium intybus

Pattern of Imbalance: Possessive of people and things; demands sympathy, love and affection; uses emotional blackmail; dislikes being alone; enjoys arguments; domineering; fussy; mentally congested; fears losing friends; feigns illness; anxious; self-centred; tearful; strong willed; saps others; house proud.

Positive Potential: Selfless love given freely; inner security and wisdom.

The Child: Demands a great deal of attention; cannot bear to be alone and may even fake or feign illness to get their own way.

CLEMATIS
Clematis vitalba

Pattern of Imbalance: A day-dreamer, with thoughts often far away in the future; lacks ambition; welcomes the prospect of death; impractical; needs a great deal of sleep; feigns illness to escape from life; is sapped by others; often artistic; sometimes mediumistic. *Clematis* is also the remedy for any bemused state of mind.

Positive Potential: If creative, as most *Clematis* types are, the ability to bring into realization creative inspiration, to take a lively interest in all things because the purpose of life can be fully appreciated.

The Child: They may be pale and sleepy, inattentive and absent-minded. They have a poor body image and tend to bump into things. Eyes are usually unfocused and expression dreamy.

CRAB APPLE
Malus pumila or *sylvestris*

Pattern of Imbalance: A feeling of being unclean; self-disgust; overemphasis on trivial detail; house proud; fussy; anxious; obsessed with imperfection; disgusted by bodily functions such as breastfeeding, sex or illness; may have a skin complaint.

Positive Potential: The wisdom to see things in their proper perspective; self respect; acceptance of the physical body.

The Child: The remedy is useful during puberty for the girl who finds menstruation distasteful or for the youngster who is embarrassed by a spotty skin or about themselves in general.

ELM
Ulmus procera

Pattern of Imbalance: Temporary feelings of inadequacy, even though fulfilling mission in life. (Compare with *Hornbeam*, whose fatigue is through dislike of their work, and with *Olive*, who is worn out by long and continued stress such as illness or a desperately unhappy situation. Elm types love their work, but need to recharge their batteries from time to time.)

Positive Potential: Joyous service; the ability to see problems in their proper perspective; an inner conviction that help will always come at the right moment.

The Child: This remedy is for the child who may be suffering from overload at examination time, even though they usually sail through their schoolwork; also for the child who must take on adult responsibilities in a dysfunctional family.

GENTIAN
Gentiana amerella

Pattern of Imbalance: Depressed through setback; easily discouraged; a 'doubting Thomas' attitude.

Positive Potential: Perseverance; the faith of a positive sceptic – one who sees difficulties, but does not fall into a deep gloom over them.

The Child: They may be discouraged by schoolwork and therefore not want to go back to school; or may be torn in two as a result of being dragged back and forth between divorced parents.

GORSE
Ulex europaeus

Pattern of Imbalance: Hopelessness and despair; may be chronically ill and feels nothing more can be done, yet *can* be persuaded to try again, albeit half-heartedly. (Compare with the *Wild Rose* type who is even more passive and apathetic and is unable to muster the enthusiasm to try again, even to please their loved ones.)

Positive Potential: The knowledge that all difficulties will be overcome in the end; glimpsing the light at the end of the tunnel.

The Child: The remedy will uplift the spirits of the child who may have become despondent as a result of long illness.

HEATHER
Calluna vulgaris

Pattern of Imbalance: Self-centred; saps others with non-stop talking; may give graphic accounts of all their illnesses; fears being alone; a poor listener; feigns illness to obtain sympathy; mentally congested; childish; weeps easily.

Positive Potential: Great empathy as a result of having suffered; a good listener; emotionally secure.

The Child: They will talk about themselves with great exuberance, exaggerating along the way! In fact, the *Heather* state of mind is a natural childhood phase and should never be deemed a problem.

HOLLY
Ilex aquifolium

Pattern of Imbalance: Feeling cut off from love. Envy, jealousy, anger and hatred; may have a violent temperament; suspicious; saps others. (Compare with *Willow*, who is an introvert, a depressive character who sees himself as a victim. *Holly* is a more active or intense type who can openly express her feelings – at least with those whom she knows well.)

Positive Potential: To feel loved and able to love others; the ability to give without thought of recompense; to rejoice in the good fortune of others.

The Child: *Holly* is a most helpful remedy during childhood, particularly when the first child is jealous of the new baby, for example.

HONEYSUCKLE
Lonicera caprifolium

Pattern of Imbalance: Nostalgic; lives in the past; suffers deep regret; homesick; often talkative; fears the ageing process; may be obsessed with past life theory to the detriment of the present life; lacks observation; often sad; saps others.

Positive Potential: The ability to retain the lessons taught by past experiences, but not to cling to memories at the expense of the present.

The Child: May suffer homesickness whilst staying with relatives or have disturbing dreams caused by a recurrent upsetting memory.

HORNBEAM
Carpinus betulus

Pattern of Imbalance: Tiredness, weariness; that 'Monday morning' feeling. Boredom or laziness.

Positive Potential: A renewed interest in life; energy and involvement in daily tasks.

The Child: This remedy will be helpful for the child who is feeling 'flat' as a result of the excitement (or strain) of returning to school after the holidays, for example, or following illness.

IMPATIENS
Impatiens glandulifera (I. roylei)

Pattern of Imbalance: Impatient and irritable; desires to work alone at own swift pace; over-works; has high ideals so finds fault with others; quick in mind and body, which often results in nervous tension and muscular pain; sometimes angry or violent.

Positive Potential: Great empathy, patience, and tolerance, especially towards the shortcomings of others. The ability to relax.

The Child: Irritable, impatient and constantly squabbling with other children; may also be prone to temper tantrums, especially if they cannot have it NOW! (However, if there is a tendency to self-injury, turn to *Cherry Plum*.)

LARCH
Larix decidua

Pattern of Imbalance: Lacks confidence; expects failure so rarely bothers to try; feigns illness to avoid responsibility; weak-willed.

Positive Potential: Bach describes *Larch* as the remedy that helps us become a little bolder so that we may plunge into life, seeking to our utmost, and in so doing, we may fulfil our purpose on Earth, which is to gain experience and knowledge.

The Child: Like the adult, feels unable to venture alone, has low self-esteem, and needs a great deal of gentle encouragement from parents, carers and teachers.

MIMULUS
Mimulus guttatus

Pattern of Imbalance: Fear of *known* things such as flying, animals, public speaking, going to the dentist and so forth (compare with *Aspen*, whose fears are less tangible).

Positive Potential: The quiet courage to face trials and difficulties; becoming understanding and supportive of others in a similar situation.

The Child: They may fear the dark, other children, animals or even the swimming pool.

MUSTARD
Sinapis arvensis

Pattern of Imbalance: Fluctuating cycles of black depression, without obvious cause.

Positive Potential: Inner serenity; the ability to transmute melancholia into joy and peace.

The Child: If a child is suffering from depression, do consult your doctor, and perhaps also seek the advice of an accredited holistic health practitioner. The remedy should only be given as a supportive measure.

OAK
Quercus robur

Pattern of Imbalance: Despondency as a result of obstinate, relentless effort against all odds; life viewed as an uphill struggle; refuses to give in to illness; may suffer nervous breakdown or collapse.

Positive Potential: Balanced strength; accepting one's limits and therefore knowing when to surrender.

The Child: Like the adult, they work very hard, viewing their schoolwork as some vital duty which must be done at all costs. Unlike *Elm*, who may momentarily lose confidence, *Oak* carries on, to the limits of endurance, even though the effort may have become useless. Consider deeply whether the child is being pushed by over-ambitious parents.

OLIVE
Olea europoea

Pattern of Imbalance: Complete mental and physical exhaustion. (Compare with *Hornbeam*, whose weariness is more of the mind, that 'Monday morning' feeling. The *Olive* exhaustion is complete, of mind and body, as a result of over-exertion during childbirth, for example, or a long illness.)

Positive Potential: Peace of mind, revitalization; a renewed interest in life.

The Child: The remedy is invaluable to children during illness and convalescence, acting as a strengthener.

PINE
Pinus sylvestris

Pattern of Imbalance: Self-reproach; guilt; blaming self for the wrongdoings of others.

Positive Potential: Self-acceptance; self-forgiveness; the ability to let go of the past; to take responsibility with a fair and balanced attitude.

The Child: Tends to be the scapegoat in class, taking the blame for the mistakes of others, accepting the punishment without complaint.

RED CHESTNUT
Aesculus carnea

Pattern of Imbalance: Fear and excessive concern for the welfare of others; always imagines the worst; is extremely distressed by reports of war, famine or other disasters; mentally congested; tense.

Positive Potential: The ability to send out thoughts of safety, health or courage to those who need them; to keep a cool head in emergencies.

The Child: They may fear that something dreadful will happen to loved ones – for example, growing anxious when the mother leaves the house. This may be a reflection of the over-anxious attitude of a parent or guardian.

ROCK ROSE
Helianthemum nummularium

Pattern of Imbalance: An extremely acute state of fear, terror or panic – at the site of a horrific accident, for example. May also help those prone to panic attacks.

(*Rock Rose* is included in the five-flower *Rescue Remedy* (see page 56). *Rescue Remedy* is more likely to be used in

emergencies than *Rock Rose* alone because many people carry a bottle of the remedy around with them for such purposes.)
Positive Potential: Great courage – the willingness to risk one's own life for others.
The Child: The remedy will help the child who wakes in a state of panic from a nightmare.

ROCK WATER
This is not a plant, but potentized spring water.
Pattern of Imbalance: Too rigid self-discipline; repression and self-denial; fixed ideas and opinions combined with perfectionism; intolerant, but rarely openly critical of others; anxious and tense; strong willed; a tendency to eating disorders; may become fanatical about a healthy lifestyle.
Positive Potential: Open-minded idealism; radiating joy and peace, thus a natural example to others; in touch with the emotional aspect of self; able to let go and enjoy!
The Child: Not a state normally associated with childhood, though the remedy may help the pernickity eater.

SCLERANTHUS
Scleranthus annus
Pattern of Imbalance: Suffers from mood swings and procrastination; tends to be unreliable; lacks concentration; lacks confidence; has weak convictions; unstable; may suffer nervous breakdown or collapse; lacks poise; restless; may have a violent temperament.
Positive Potential: The ability to make a decision quickly and to act promptly; to maintain poise and balance whatever the circumstances.
The Child: Like the adult, the child is subject to extremes of mood, crying one minute, smiling the next. During illness

symptoms move about or swing from one polarity to the other; constipation then diarrhoea, hot then cold; ravenous hunger then loss of appetite, and so on.

STAR OF BETHLEHEM
Ornithogalum umbellatum

Pattern of Imbalance: Shock or trauma, either recent or from a past experience; grief; emotional numbness.

(The effects of shock can be so delayed that many years might pass before the full impact is felt. It may manifest as feelings of guilt, depression, anxiety or anger, or perhaps in the guise of some physical complaint. In such cases, *Star of Bethlehem* can often be the catalyst required if shock or trauma has been sustained and can be identified as the cause of the present distress. To identify whether past shock is a cause, go back over your life and consider all the major upheavals in order to ascertain whether or not the distress was fully released at the time. When counselling another person, encourage them to do the same.)

Positive Potential: A neutralization of the effect of shock, whether immediate or delayed.

The Child: The remedy can be used for deep shock or trauma such as divorce or the death of a parent. It can also be given to newborn babies (perhaps in the baby's bath water) to help neutralize the shock of entering the world.

SWEET CHESTNUT
Castanea sativa

Pattern of Imbalance: Extreme mental anguish, perhaps triggered by some life-shattering event; the utmost limits of endurance; paroxysm of grief; feeling utterly alone; unable even to pray.

Positive Potential: Hope returns; the end of torment is at last within reach. Personal experiences of the true meaning of life, and/or of the Godhead.

The Child: For times during illness when the emotional agony or strain seems to be too much to bear and the child does not know which way to turn. The remedy may also be indicated for the child suffering mental anguish as a result of parental divorce or bereavement.

VERVAIN
Verbena officinalis

Pattern of Imbalance: Strain and tension as a result of over-enthusiasm; a tendency to hyperactivity; missionary zeal; a tendency to interfere in the affairs of others; talkative; a martyr to the cause; rigid in mind and body; may suffer nervous breakdown or collapse.

Positive Potential: The realization that others have the right to their opinions; the wisdom to change one's mind as a result of discussion and debate; the ability to relax once in a while.

The Child: The child is tense and frustrated, perhaps also hyperactive; has difficulty sleeping or needs less sleep than average.

VINE
Vitis vinifera

Pattern of Imbalance: A domineering and inflexible personality; intolerant; lacks sympathy; violent temperament.

Positive Potential: The wise and compassionate leader who inspires others; the ability to use great qualities of leadership to guide rather than to dominate.

The Child: This child is always the leader of the gang or the school captain; tends to be aggressive and in the extreme can become a bully.

WALNUT
Juglans regia

Pattern of Imbalance: Difficulties adjusting to change of any nature; sometimes held-back or misguided by others; feels 'stuck' in present situation, yet desires to move on (compare with *Honeysuckle* who yearns for the past).

(The remedy can also be used for easing the transitions of puberty, pregnancy and the menopause (see Chapter 5).)

Positive Potential: Freedom from limiting circumstances; the courage to carry through one's ideals and ambitions despite adverse circumstances, damning comments and ridicule.

The Child: The remedy is helpful during the various milestones of a child's development – teething, starting school, and puberty, for instance.

WATER VIOLET
Hottonia palustris

Pattern of Imbalance: Proud and aloof; disdainful of social relationships; suffers in silence; physical rigidity; radiates superiority.

Positive Potential: Although remaining serene and self-contained, has the wisdom and sympathy to put own capabilities to the service of others.

The Child: Appears withdrawn and arrogant through being unable to communicate well; can spend many hours alone, playing contentedly.

WHITE CHESTNUT
Aesculus hippocastanum
Pattern of Imbalance: Persistent worrying thoughts and mental arguments; may suffer from insomnia; lacks observation; worried.

Positive Potential: Peace of mind and a solution to problems.

The Child: The children needing this remedy have trouble clearing their mind of worries and argument. They recognize that their thoughts are repetitive and want to stop, but cannot.

WILD OAT
Bromus ramosus
Pattern of Imbalance: Dissatisfaction because one's true vocation has not been found; boredom and frustration; a 'Jack of all trades, master of none.'

Positive Potential: The realization of one's true vocation.

The Child: This child is usually very able but, like the adult, tends to scatter their energies, rarely identifying with any particular peer group. The remedy is also useful for the teenager trying to make up their mind which subjects to take for final school examinations.

WILD ROSE
Rosa canina
Pattern of Imbalance: Apathy and resignation; 'I'll have to live with it' attitude; neither happy nor unhappy; emotionally 'flat'.

Positive Potential: A renewed interest in life and, with the return of one's vitality, the enrichment and enjoyment of friendship and good health.

The Child: Do seek advice from your health practitioner if this state of mind has become chronic. It is common for a mild *Wild Rose* state to emerge after illness, though it is usually a passing phase.

WILLOW
Salix viminalis

Pattern of Imbalance: Bitter and resentful – 'poor me' attitude; selfish; enjoys arguments; blames others; grumpy and morose; may simulate illness to obtain pity; irritable and sulky.

Positive Potential: Optimism and a sense of humour; the ability to accept responsibility for one's own life and health, and to see things in their true perspective.

The Child: These children are sulky and resentful, but the reason for the distress is not always apparent. When lightly scolded for some misdemeanour, they feel they do not deserve so great a punishment.

The Californian Essences

ALPINE LILY
Datura candida

Uses: A helpful remedy during adolescence (and also for older women) where there may be distress about menstruation and breast development (or lack of development!), perhaps as a result of the mother's negative attitude to her own body or from cultural influences.

Positive Potential: Positive acceptance of one's femininity.

ANGEL'S TRUMPET
Datura candida

Uses: This is the key remedy for the dying person, especially if there is fear and resistance to crossing the threshold. The essence is helpful in hospice work, in wartime, during natural disasters and on all occasions when we are called upon to minister to loved ones shortly before their parting.

Positive Potential: Spiritual surrender.

CHAMOMILE
Anthemis cotula

Uses: For those who are easily upset, moody and irritable, unable to release emotional tension, especially anger, and anxiety. It is also an excellent remedy for insomnia and indeed for all forms of stress, including that experienced during the pre-menstrual phase or at menopause. *Chamomile* can be safely used during pregnancy and for babies and children. The remedy can also be added to a relaxing aromatherapy massage oil or added to an aromatic bath, thus broadening the psychotherapeutic effects of the aroma.

Positive Potential: Serenity; a sunny disposition; emotional balance.

CORN
Zea mays

Uses: This is the remedy for the stress of urban living. An extremely helpful essence for the harassed mother living in cramped quarters, or in high density housing, especially if she craves spaciousness and dreams of living close to the Earth. The remedy can also be given to children similarly suffering from the effects of overcrowding.

Positive Potential: A grounded sense of peacefulness and space despite living in an urban environment.

MALLOW
Sidalcea

Uses: This is the remedy for those who feel insecure and are afraid to reach out to others. Such a personality has not learned to trust others or to trust their own capacity to radiate warmth and friendliness. A remedy which is often useful in adolescence.

Positive Potential: An open-hearted sharing and friendliness.

MARIPOSA LILY
Calochortus leichtlinii

Uses: For those who feel alienated from their mother due to abandonment, abuse or trauma in childhood and are thus themselves unable to show nurturing and caring attention to others. Also helpful during adolescence when there may be stormy periods with the mother or other female figures.

Positive Potential: The healing of trauma and the expression of nurturing love; healing of the 'inner child'.

POMEGRANATE
Punica granatum

Uses: This is the remedy supreme for all women. It is a hormone balancer and is therefore helpful in adolescence, for pre-menstrual syndrome, emotionally induced infertility and menopausal problems. The remedy is also indicated for men who feel they need to become more in touch with the nurturing side of their nature. *Pomegranate* also engenders clarity in those women who feel torn between home and career.

Positive Potential: A positive sense of one's femininity; an enhanced sense of nurturing; the ability to see more clearly which choices to make or how happily to compromise.

PRETTY FACE
Triteleia ixioides

Uses: For those who feel unattractive or ugly, or over-identified with their physical appearance. It is also the remedy for those who fear the ageing process. *Pretty Face* can often be helpful in certain cases of anorexia, bulimia and obesity.

Positive Potential: Beauty that radiates from within; self-acceptance in relation to personal appearance.

SUNFLOWER
Helianthus annus

Uses: For those who have low self-esteem or, on the contrary, are prone to vanity and self-aggrandizement. While some people mask their true sun nature with self-effacement and low self-esteem, others want their brilliance to shine too strongly, glaring others with their pompous self-glory. So the woman who needs *Sunflower* has a poor relationship with the masculine or outgoing side of self. Moreover, chances are that she may have experienced a deficient childhood relationship with her father. Incidentally, while *Sunflower* is a wonderful remedy for women, the healing of the masculine self is equally important for men too.

Positive Potential: The remedy brings out the sun-like qualities of the shining, expressive self, but in a balanced way.

The Australian Bush Essences

BILLY GOAT PLUM
Planchonia careya

Uses: For those who suffer feelings of self-disgust or self-loathing, especially when this is centred on the sexual organs and/or the sexual act. Those who have been raped (and this includes homosexual rape) are often left with the sense that their bodies are dirty. Of course, specialized counselling is also necessary in this instance.

The remedy can also be applied externally and/or taken internally for healing the emotional causes of skin complaints such as eczema or psoriasis, but only if the disorder elicits a sense of the body being unclean.

Positive Potential: The remedy helps to bring about a real acceptance of the physical body and the ability to enjoy physical sensations and a sexual relationship.

BUSH FUCHSIA
Epacris longiflora

Uses: For children and adults suffering from learning difficulties such as dyslexia. The remedy makes learning fun. It also increases clarity of speech, so is most helpful for stutterers and public speakers.

Positive Potential: The remedy balances the left and right hemispheres of the brain, thus communication becomes much easier.

LITTLE FLANNEL FLOWER
Actinotus minor

Uses: This remedy embraces the 'inner child'. It engenders an expression of playfulness and joy. A wonderful remedy for parents, allowing them to lose some of their inhibitions and to play and have fun with their children. The remedy can also be given to the rather morose child who has become old before their time, perhaps taking on the troubles of the world.

Positive Potential: To allow that playful child within to emerge from the serious depths of adulthood.

SHE OAK
Casuraina glauca

Uses: One of the most important flower essences for hormonal imbalances in females. Ian White, founder of the Bush Flower Essences, has had a great deal of success with this remedy in cases of emotionally induced infertility. The remedy is also be helpful for women suffering from fluid retention and PMS.

Positive Potential: Hormonal balance.

Chapter Five

A WOMAN FOR ALL SEASONS

Flower Remedies for Life

In this chapter you will find a number of flower essence combinations (or single essences) which I believe women of all ages and all walks of life will find most helpful. Do remember, however, that flower therapy should go far beyond the 'standard prescription' level. Therefore, when taking a suggested remedy (or mixture) for a specific problem, it is also important to personalize the prescription by selecting one other remedy which closely çorresponds to your personality and/or present emotional state (refer to the information in Chapters 3 and 4).

When treating yourself or others, do try to recognize your own or the other person's limitations and, as already mentioned, seek professional help where necessary in the form of counselling or a physical approach such as nutritional advice, massage, herbal medicine or orthodox treatment. Moreover, it cannot be emphasized enough that the flower essences are not a *replacement* for a healthy diet and sensible lifestyle, rather they should be regarded as a *natural adjunct* to these things. Also, in common with all natural treatments, flower remedies work far more efficiently if your body is not overloaded with the debris of a junk-food diet, cigarette smoking and other potentially damaging habits.

The Female Life-Cycle

Women have always recognized their own nature in the moon, their periodicity being measured in approximately 28-day cycles, corresponding to the lunar tides. (Incidentally, men have cycles too, measured not by ovulation and blood flow, but by weight loss and changes in albumen content of the urine.) We are also pulled by the rhythms of day and night, inhalation and exhalation, birth and death, and by the seasons – spring and autumn, summer and winter. Poetic licence granted, let us for a moment equate the female life-cycle to the phases of the moon and the changing seasons:

Early spring and the new moon heralds the time of the young girl's awakening. Emerging from the lapping waters of childhood, she is drawn by the swell of the spring tides. As the currents of change swirl her back and forth, her moods swing from elation to despair, from childish dependence to sudden adult insight . . . And with the approach of summer, the warmth of the masculine sun caresses the depths of her being, and new life is conceived within a tranquil sea. Under the light of the full moon she gives birth, and recognizes her nature in the fruitful Earth. Her mother love is all-embracing, sheltering and nurturing . . . With the approach of autumn and the waning moon, she mourns the passing of a loved one, and yearns for that which has been, and for that which might have been. And just when it seems all is lost, the emerging Wise Woman beckons her forth from the moon shadow, into the golden light of dawn . . . At dark moon when the first snows of winter blanket the slumbering Earth, the old Wise Woman sits by the hearth-fire enchanting her grandchildren with stories of life and love. She is happy to look back, yet no

longer fears what lies ahead . . . And so she crosses the
threshold, surrendering to the light of the spiritual sun . . .

Seasonal Affective Disorder

You may be wondering why I have launched into SAD
('winter depression') at this point when it is not directly
related to the female life-cycle, for men can be affected too. As
a matter of interest, statistics show that the vast majority of
sufferers are pre-menopausal women. Perhaps this is because
the condition intensifies during the pre-menstrual phase, as
does any form of distress, due to increased sensitivity
associated with hormonal fluctuations. But what exactly is
SAD and how can flower therapy help?

Psychiatrists first became aware that some people suffer
severe winter depression as a result of light deprivation half a
century ago, but seasonal affective disorder (SAD), as it is now
called, has only recently been treated seriously. Symptoms
include lethargy, irritability, loss of libido and self-esteem,
mood changes, overeating and what can best be described as
'sleepaholism'. The gloom begins to descend in the autumn,
reaching an all time low mid-winter, only to magically lift
again with the first rays of the spring sunshine.

SAD sufferers are hypersensitive to reduced sunlight. When
light enters our eyes it strikes the pineal gland at the base of
the brain, which secretes melatonin – the substance which
affects sleep, mood and the reproductive cycle. Usually levels
of melatonin rise at night and subside at dawn. In SAD,
melatonin production happens later at night than usual,
resulting in a 'sleep hangover' and those all-day blues.

If you are a sufferer of SAD, and are forced to spend a great
deal of time indoors, it might be worth investing in some full-
spectrum lighting – that which mimics natural daylight.

Severe cases respond best to very bright light emitted from a purpose-designed unit or 'light-box'. The sufferer basks in front of the light first thing in the morning, which serves to kick-start the body for the rest of the day. Studies have shown that full-spectrum light treatment (phototherapy) has an impressive 85 per cent success rate. Full-spectrum lightbulbs and light-boxes can be obtained by mail order (see Useful Addresses on page 124).

It is also important to get out in the fresh air as often as possible. Even though it may require a superhuman effort, try to walk in the countryside or the local park for at least an hour each day. Exercise also helps combat another symptom of SAD – excessive weight gain (see also the yoga 'Sun Salutation' on pages 116–18).

As a sufferer of a mild form of SAD myself, I have found the Californian flower essences *Sunflower* and *Chamomile* helpful, along with the Bach Remedy *Mustard*. (The Flower Essence Society suggests *St John's Wort* essence.)

In addition to taking flower essences, you may also find home aromatherapy treatments helpful and enjoyable. Any of the bright and cheery essential oils listed below are recommended (choose according to your aroma preference). Add up to six drops of essential oil (along with a few drops of the flower essences if you wish) to your bath, or take an invigorating shower and massage the oils and flower essences into your skin afterwards.

To prepare a massage oil, add no more than two drops of essential oil per teaspoonful of a good quality vegetable oil, preferably cold pressed olive, known as 'extra virgin'. Rub the oil all over your body two or three times a week, always after a bath or shower when the skin is warm and moist, and thus more capable of absorbing the oils.

Suggested Essential Oils: Bergamot, coriander, geranium, grapefruit, lemon, mandarin, neroli, orange, rose, rosemary.

Adolescence

The transitional period between childhood and adulthood can be a painful experience for the young person of either sex, and just as painful for any parent who, for the most part, can only stand in the wings and watch. For the adolescent has awakened to the realization that they are an individual in their own right, not just the child of their parents. The difficulty for parents is in learning to come to terms with their child's pulling away from adult influence and control.

For the young girl, menarche (first menstruation) heralds her passage into womanhood. If she has been properly prepared for the event, then her first period should not be a distressing experience. Even though it may take a while for her to adapt both physically and emotionally to the changes taking place in her body, she will also feel proud of her burgeoning womanhood. However, if her first period comes without warning, perhaps because she is much younger than the average age of menarche, which normally begins at around 12 to 14 years of age, she may suffer an appalling amount of fear and distress. After all, blood is usually associated with wounds and disease. This, coupled with the shock and embarrassment of coping with a changing body, can distort the way a woman may feel about herself for the rest of her life.

Those mothers who are ashamed, anxious and embarrassed about discussing menstruation and conception instil into their daughters the same fear and confusion. However, in families that have always been open and expressive about physical and emotional matters, youngsters (whether boys or girls) will emerge from adolescence totally unscathed by the experience. Moreover, they will not shy away from sharing their problems with their parents and other trusted adults.

Suggested Flower Essences
Generally speaking, a combination of *Pomegranate* (a female hormone balancer), *Mallow* (for feelings of insecurity), *Scleranthus* (for mood swings) and *Walnut* (to help with the transition) is a good choice and can be taken on and off as required throughout adolescence. Other useful remedies include:

- *Alpine Lily* – for a healthy relationship to menstruation and breast development.
- *Billy Goat Plum* – similar to *Crab Apple*, but being an Australian essence, its effects may be more pronounced.
- *Chamomile* – another remedy for rapid mood swings, which can be used instead of *Scleranthus*, especially if the remedy profile more accurately corresponds to the youngster's emotional state.
- *Chamomile* is also a helpful remedy for menstrual cramp, which is particularly common in young girls. Of course, *Chamomile* will ease period pain whatever a woman's age. If this does not work, regular massage, with particular emphasis to the lower back, with aromatherapy oils such as chamomile, clary sage, rose or lavender may help. Homoeopathic remedies may also be beneficial. However, should the pain be severe and prolonged, it is important to seek medical advice as there may be a serious underlying health problem.
    Chamomile is also useful for sleeplessness, broken-heartedness and anger.
- *Crab Apple* – for self-disgust about acne or other feelings of ugliness or shame about the body and/or its functions.
- *Elm* – for youngsters suffering a temporary crisis due to pressure of work or exams.

- *Larch* – for lack of confidence.
- *Mariposa Lily* – for stormy periods with the mother or other female figures; for too early onset of puberty in girls or boys.
- *Mimulus* – for exam nerves.
- *Oak* – in relation to schoolwork, for a feeling that everything is an uphill struggle and that no matter how hard one works, there are no tangible results.
- *Pretty Face* – for self-consciousness due to concern about physical appearance.
- *Sweet Chestnut* – for healing the broken-heartedness associated with romantic trauma, especially that which is experienced for the first time.
- *Sunflower* – for the development of positive individuality (in boys as well as girls), especially where there is a poor or non-existent relationship with the father.
- *Wild Oat* – for confusion about goals in life, especially when having to decide which subjects to take up for the final school examinations.
- *Willow* – for resentment and bitterness; a feeling that life is unfair; blaming parents and figures of authority.

Parents who have difficulty coming to terms with their youngster's pulling away as they search for an adult identity can also take the transitional remedy *Walnut*. In addition, if there is a great deal of over-fretful concern for a son or daughter, then *Red Chestnut* is indicated. For parents embarrassed about discussing menstruation and conception with their daughters, a mixture of *Crab Apple* (or *Billy Goat Plum*) and *Mimulus* will give the courage to discuss such matters openly.

Eating Disorders

One of the most pernicious maladies of our times, and one which claims young girls in particular (though boys are not immune), must surely be anorexia nervosa and the related eating disorder bulimia (binge eating followed by purging and vomiting). One long-held theory is that self-starvation is a rejection of womanhood and that adolescent girls use it as a way of warding off maturity, of preventing breast growth, menstruation and, thereby, conception. It is also about control. The longing for both control of their bodies and their lives becomes intense and confused.

According to the Royal College of Psychiatrists, 1 in every 100 schoolgirls in Britain suffers from anorexia to a greater or lesser degree. Two in every 100 women aged between 15 and 45 have bulimia. There are high rates of both anorexia and bulimia among models, dancers and those in media-related jobs.

Whatever the underlying cause, the greatest pressure must surely come from modern society's obsession with the Body Beautiful – an impossibly thin ideal promoted by women's magazines and the fashion industry, and one which few women can achieve without a masochistic regime of self-denial and hunger. Indeed, those responsible for promoting the 'ideal' image of women are often sick themselves. Jane Fonda, for instance, suffered from bulimia for many years, and Princess Diana, a paragon of modern feminine beauty, is also struggling to overcome the bingeing and vomiting cycle of self-starvation.

Even more disturbing, pre-adolescent dieting is on the increase. Born to compete, little girls, sometimes as young as six or seven, have been taught by their mother's example to associate femaleness with deprivation. Hunger is regarded as a prerequisite for entering into adult sexuality. This is an alarming state of affairs, which leads one to conclude that Western society is suffering from nothing less than an insidious neurosis triggered by 'Beauty Pornography', as feminist writer Naomi Wolf so aptly describes it.

While flower remedies can help both mother and daughter to overcome their eating problems, especially in the early stages, it is also important to seek the aid of a specialist counsellor or a support group, for the problem is often deep-rooted, involving the whole family.

Suggested Flower Essences
- *Cherry Plum* – for feeling out of control about eating; for bingeing and purging cycles.
- *Crab Apple* – for the excessive need for cleansing diets or purgatives.
- *Pretty Face* – for a distorted sense of physical appearance; creating a false image of extreme fatness (or even thinness!)
- *Rock Water* – for an overly strict exercise or dietary regime.

Pre-Menstrual Syndrome (PMS)

THE CONDITION

This condition was previously called PMT (pre-menstrual tension), however 'syndrome' is a more apt term because tension is but one of many symptoms, both emotional and physical. PMS can begin at any time from two days to two weeks before menstruation. Physical symptoms can include fluid retention, weight gain, bloating, constipation, breast tenderness, headaches, nausea, disturbed sleep and skin eruptions. As well as tension, there may be other psychological symptoms such as lethargy, depression, low self-esteem, food cravings, tearfulness and irritability. Luckily, very few women suffer all these symptoms, but all women experience some degree of pre-menstrual change.

Interestingly, the pre-menstrual phase can also be a time of heightened creativity and deeper insight (this was the experience of Virginia Woolf, for instance). Then there are those women who experience a surge of energy at this time, the kind of energy that enables them to take on projects that would normally tax several workers! After the gush of energy, however, they usually feel totally drained.

THE CAUSES

But what causes PMS? A few esoteric healers, though not Bach, have suggested that the condition is a 'rejection of the feminine processes'. This rings of Freud's 'penis envy' – another fallacy? True, body and mind are interrelated, therefore negative feelings about our femininity may well affect certain physiological processes. However, since many thousands – and possibly millions – of women suffer from PMS, surely negative thinking cannot be the sole cause?

It is my own belief that a certain degree of PMS – and I do not include suicidal or murderous tendencies here – is a perfectly reasonable response by a healthy reproductive system to the unnatural state of non-pregnancy. Before you gasp in horror, I am not for a moment suggesting that women should give in to biology; rather I am saying that PMS is at least partly physical in origin (unless one views contraception, celibacy or lesbianism as a rejection of the feminine processes). Interestingly, native women rarely get the chance to be pre-menstrual because during their fertile years they are usually pregnant or breastfeeding (breastfeeding can delay the onset of menstruation for up to three years). Moreover, since menstruation is taboo in many primitive patriarchal societies, it may be just as well that the women do not experience it very often. Such negative conditioning is hardly conducive to care-free bleeding!

The real culprit in PMS is fluid retention, caused by natural changes in body chemistry. PMS is also exacerbated by stress and a poor diet which is why it can, to a great extent, be remedied – as so many women have discovered. Moreover, we can use flower essences as an adjunct to other common sense measures.

Suggested Flower Essences

As with all 'female problems', *Pomegranate* should be your first choice. However, I have also been impressed with the effects of the Australian Bush essence *She Oak*. According to Ian White (founder of the Bush essences), a number of gynaecologists now use the *She Oak* essence to treat hormonal imbalances, including PMS. For the first three months it is important to take the remedy (either *Pomegranate* or *She Oak*) twice a day throughout the cycle. It can take this long for the essence to begin taking effect. Thereafter, you may only need to take the remedy during the pre-menstrual phase, usually a week to 10 days prior to menstruation. At this stage, you may also need to include one or two other remedies according to your needs:

- *Chamomile* – for mood swings, insomnia, emotional tension.
- *Impatiens* – for impatience, irritation, tension and intolerance.
- *Mustard* – for severe depression and despair.
- *Olive* – for physical and emotional exhaustion.
- *Pretty Face* – for those who feel ugly or rejected because of their physical appearance.
- *Scleranthus* – for mood swings.
- *Sunflower* – for low self-esteem and self-effacement.

Pregnancy and Childbirth

As the renowned herbalist Juliette de Bairacli-Lévy so beautifully put it, 'Pregnancy should be a daily song of triumph and thanksgiving in a woman's mind and heart.' From my own experience, once the first two months of tiredness and morning sickness have abated, pregnancy can certainly be a time of enhanced awareness and creativity. The senses become heightened, especially taste and smell – this is the reason why eating habits may change at this time. In late pregnancy, most women feel quite placid due to the staggeringly high level of the hormone progesterone in the bloodstream. However, if there is a great deal of stress in a woman's life, pregnancy may be far from joyful. As well as suffering from numerous physical ailments, she will feel extremely tired and irritable, and the quietness of the third trimester may well be experienced as depression.

After birth, progesterone and other hormones fall precipitously, which is the reason why many women suffer from 'baby blues' for a few days after delivery. However, some women may develop full-blown depression lasting many weeks or months following childbirth (or as a result of miscarriage or abortion). Although the problem is largely attributed to hormonal imbalance, it is also related to high levels of stress, poor health, changes in lifestyle and social status, immediate separation from the baby after birth, an unexpected Caesarean, over-sedation during the birth and many other interrelated factors. Whatever the combination of causes, as well as taking the flower remedies it is advisable to seek guidance and support from your health visitor or health practitioner.

Suggested Flower Essences

Many flower essences, especially the Bach Remedies, are perfectly safe and highly beneficial to the expectant mother and her unborn child. They can be of help where there is apprehension or emotional suffering during the pre- and post-natal periods. A number of Bach Flower Remedy practitioners suggest a basic composite of *Rescue Remedy* and *Walnut*. This mixture can be taken a few days before the expected date of delivery, during labour and for about a month afterwards to help both mother and child cope with reaction and change.

Incidentally, flower remedy practitioner George Vlamis has collected a great deal of data recording cases of mothers having experienced an easy and gentle birth and a rapid recovery as a result of taking *Rescue Remedy* shortly before parturition. During labour, *Oak*, *Hornbeam* and *Olive* may be indicated if the woman is exhausted and feels she can no longer carry on; and during the post-natal period *Mustard*, *Gorse*, *Gentian*, *Sweet Chestnut* or *Willow* may have a role to play in uplifting the spirits of the mother suffering from 'baby blues'.

Other Helpful Flower Essences
- *Alpine Lily* – to enable one to experience conception and pregnancy as positive states.
- *Chamomile* – for the emotional ups and downs of pregnancy; nausea and stomach upset.
- *Impatiens* – to help those who become irritable and impatient as they near term (especially helpful when the baby is overdue).
- *Mariposa Lily* – to enhance bonding between mother and child; to engender confidence about mothering.
- *Mimulus* – for fear of childbirth (in extreme cases, use *Rock Rose*).

- *Olive* – for fatigue from lost sleep; exhaustion from prolonged labour.
- *Pomegranate* – for conflicts between career and home life.
- *Red Chestnut* – for over-worry and concern about pregnancy or the newborn baby.

Babies

Generally speaking, it is best to use only the Bach Flower Remedies for babies, unless you are under the guidance of an experienced flower remedy practitioner. Try not to give more than three remedies at a time. In my own experience, babies and young children are extremely sensitive to the remedies. If given too many at a time, they may become irritable or fractious. However, the five-flower Bach *Rescue Remedy* is an exception to the rule, for it is a carefully balanced formula. In fact, *Rescue Remedy* (also *Star of Bethlehem*, one of the five flowers) can be given to newborn babies (perhaps in their bathwater) to neutralize the shock of entering the world.

The only flower remedy from the other repertories I would recommend for unsupervised home use is the Californian essence *Chamomile*. It is a wonderful remedy for the baby who is irritable, fractious and unable to sleep.

Even though babies are unable to tell us about their state of mind, it is still possible to assess their needs. For example, the *Agrimony* baby is usually happy and gurgling and is very little trouble, unless there is something definitely wrong; the *Chicory* baby is very demanding, always wanting attention and hating to be alone; the *Clematis* baby, on the other hand, shows very little interest in anything, sleeping a great deal and sometimes having to be woken for feeds; the *Mimulus* baby is very nervous, frightened by loud noises and sudden movements; while the *Impatiens* baby has quite a little temper!

Bach believed that by addressing the baby's type or personality difficulty, the passing moods or negative states of mind would be easily transmuted before they began to take root. The dosage is the same as for adults, though nursing mothers can take the remedy themselves (see page 54).

Children

Children are a joy for the flower essence practitioner for they often respond rapidly and extremely well to the remedies. This is because the young child tends to express his or her feelings openly – that is, until the self-conscious phase of adolescence. Adults, of course, are not only conditioned by society, but also by their own habitual responses to the ups and downs of life, particularly the downs. The pattern of distress then becomes deeply ingrained and thus more difficult to transmute.

If you are using the Bach Flower Remedies, first try to establish the child's type remedy if you can (see page 43). This will be required at intervals throughout childhood and indeed into maturity, unless the personality changes radically (not an unknown phenomenon). Then establish which other remedies will be supportive. For example: *Walnut*, the remedy for change and transition, is helpful during the various milestones of a child's development (teething, starting school and puberty, for instance); *Vine* will help transmute the aggressive energy of the school bully into positive qualities of leadership; *Centaury*, on the other hand, will help the bully's victim! *Holly* will embrace the child who is jealous of their baby brother or sister, while *Rock Rose* will dispel their nightmares. If the child's disturbing dreams are caused by a recurrent upsetting memory, then a mixture of *Rock Rose* and *Honeysuckle* is indicated, otherwise give *Rescue Remedy*, which contains the former two remedies. For fear of the dark, consider *Mimulus*; for vague fears of unknown origin, especially if accompanied by sweating and trembling, turn to *Aspen*; for the wakeful, highly active child, choose *Vervain*; and for the drowsy, apathetic child prescribe *Clematis*. For the long-suffering, over-anxious parent, *Red Chestnut* will engender a sense of calm and positivity.

As for babies, it is advisable not to give young children (or highly sensitive older children) more than three remedies at a time, otherwise the effect may be counter-productive, possibly leading to a sense of being overwhelmed. (For further information on prescribing for children, see the note headed *The Child* at the end of each Bach Flower Remedy profile in Chapter 4.)

Other Helpful Flower Essences
- *Bush Fuchsia* – for dyslexia or poor learning ability.
- *Chamomile* – for the hyperactive child.
- *Little Flannel Flower* – for the child who has become old before their time, perhaps through deprivation in a dysfunctional family.
- *Sunflower* – to help develop a healthy sense of self, especially if the relationship with the father is disturbed or non-existent.

Menopause

Sadly, many women dread the onset of the menopause, as if it were somehow the beginning of a grey avenue of mental and physical deterioration heightened by the loss of their sexuality and, hence, their worth as women. Such attitudes are fuelled by society's obsession with the cult of youth eternal. Instead of 'growing old gracefully', many women pathetically grab at cosmetic surgery, high-tech fertility treatments (it is now possible for women in their late fifties and early sixties to give birth!), stringent diets and punishing exercise regimes in an attempt to preserve their youth (men, of course, are not immune to some of these practices either). By taking the rich and famous as their role models (the result of media brainwashing), no wonder the average woman on a modest income is less than satisfied with her own *natural* appearance.

HORMONE REPLACEMENT THERAPY

What about hormone replacement therapy? While it would be wrong to rule out HRT completely, very few women really need to take such drastic measures. True, HRT does offer some protection against osteoporosis, or 'thinning of the bones', which is believed to be a consequence of the ovaries ceasing to function. However, oestrogen deficiency is not the sole cause, for not all post-menopausal women develop the condition. Moreover, osteoporosis can also develop in elderly men. Some authorities believe that HRT increases the risk of breast cancer in some women; also contrary to what you may have heard, HRT is not the elixir of youth. There is no evidence to support the view that it increases libido and prevents wrinkles. Indeed, I know several women for whom HRT has proved far from beneficial. Some complain of depression or nausea since starting the treatment, while others report that they simply do not feel 'normal' on HRT. No matter what the drug companies may say to the contrary, we do not know the long-term consequences of interfering with female hormones in this manner. From the naturopathic ('nature cure') perspective, it is far better to balance our hormones through supernutrition and a healthy lifestyle – and this *can* be achieved. So if you would prefer to avoid HRT unless absolutely necessary, do obtain a copy of Arabella Melville's excellent book entitled *Natural Hormone Health* which offers a drug-free alternative to managing the female life-cycle.

CULTURAL INFLUENCES

There is some evidence that the degree of difficulty experienced with the menopause is culturally determined. Anthropologists Margaret Mead and Judith K. Brown have looked at the status of women in many 'primitive' patriarchal cultures throughout the world and have found one constant: the menopause marks the threshold of seniority and rank. Women at this time are eligible for special roles within the community such as midwives, healers, givers of initiation, holy women and matchmakers. In other words, they are valued as Wise Women. Conversely, Western society views the menopause as an end, so it is not surprising that it should be a time of mourning for a great many women.

However, not all women in Western society suffer at menopause. Research suggests that those who sail through this phase without any problems at all tend to feel secure in their jobs and/or relationships, and therefore they feel valued as people. However, it would be wrong to conclude that all menopausal symptoms are caused by our negative attitudes to life. As we have already seen with PMS, body and mind are inseparably linked, so natural hormonal upheavals are bound to cause a certain degree of emotional and physical discomfort.

SYMPTOMS

The menopause can begin at any time between the ages of 42 and 50 years of age. Symptoms include the 'hot flush' (caused by a rush of hormones into the bloodstream), night sweats, mood swings, weight gain, palpitations, vaginal dryness, headaches and many other minor ailments. No wonder some women suffer from irritability, poor concentration and insomnia as well. However, it should be emphasized that few women experience *every* symptom associated with the menopause.

Anxiety and depression can often be triggered by the fact that children are likely to be growing up and leaving home, in many cases leaving their mother feeling somehow redundant. Or there may be conflict with adolescent youngsters or a woman's husband may be undergoing his own midlife crisis. Moreover, it is also common to lose a parent at around this time of life, hence grief is likely to exacerbate existing menopausal symptoms. Sometimes, then, the menopause may well get the blame when a life crisis is really at the root of the trouble.

The transition of menopause is a time for accepting our own mortality and realizing that we have to get on with anything still left to do. It is also about achieving a sense of freedom and responsibility for ourselves. Interestingly, many women return to their studies (or begin to study for the first time!) at this stage of life, often achieving far more than they ever dreamed possible. (Indeed, women are champions at underestimating their capabilities.)

Suggested Flower Essences
To help balance female hormones, *Pomegranate* can be taken once or twice a day for as long as required. (If symptoms are exacerbated by the loss of a loved one, see also the suggested remedies for bereavement on page 108.) In addition, any of the following essences may be helpful from time to time:

- *Chamomile* – for mood swings, irritability and emotional tension.

- *Crab Apple* – for a feeling of shame and self-disgust about the body and its imperfections.
- *Holly* – for feeling unloved; jealousy of younger women.
- *Honeysuckle* – for deep regret at the passing of one's youth.
- *Impatiens* – for those who are impatient, irritable and tense; intolerance.
- *Larch* – for lack of confidence.
- *Olive* – for physical and mental exhaustion.
- *Pretty Face* – for preoccupation with the idea of cosmetic surgery to attain a youthful appearance.
- *Sunflower* – for those women who feel a need to discover their more 'masculine' selves, thus enabling them to become more action-orientated, assertive or ambitious.
- *Walnut* – the transitional remedy which aids a smooth passage through to the next phase of life.

Old Age

While 'growing up' is normally considered desirable, 'growing old' has, traditionally, had very negative connotations, at least in Western society. Our prejudices against the elderly are built into everyday expressions such as 'old hag', which we often use without being aware of the attitudes on which they are based. Yet, as touched upon earlier, in many 'primitive' cultures elderly women as well as men enjoy a high social status, mainly related to their being seen as a repository of wisdom.

Even those psychologists and health writers who try to present the positive features of growing old may, inadvertently, be guilty of ageism. Many times we read words to the effect that 'successful ageing' is about continuing to behave as we did when we were younger, that is to say, middle-aged. This assumes that one age group's pattern of behaviour is somehow inherently superior to that of another and is, therefore, a value judgement which merely reinforces the idea of 'younger' being more desirable than 'older'.

Ageing is not a uniform process; we tend to age jerkily. Moreover, not everyone experiences to the same degree every problem associated with ageing – problems such as decreased bone and muscle mass, slower response or reaction time, short-term memory deterioration, wrinkling and sagging of the skin, stiff joints and physical weakness. While there is some genetic predisposition towards enjoying a long and healthy life, it is generally agreed that a healthy diet and lifestyle enhances our experience of the ageing process. Indeed, studies have shown that most negative responses to ageing are related to poor health. As long as we can maintain our health, continue to develop new interests and have an adequate income, late autumn and winter can be an incredibly satisfying stage in our lives, especially if we possess a strong sense of purpose and meaning.

An interesting study was made in 1965 of 23 Hungarian centenarians, most of whom were vegetarians. The poor souls were put into an old people's home and given a traditional diet which included meat, canned foods and sugar. They quickly started to deteriorate, began fumbling, had trouble remembering things and usually died from thrombosis. I suspect that the meaningless existence of institutional life played a great part in the breakdown of their physical and mental well-being.

One very important change that many elderly women will experience is the loss of their spouse of up to 40 or 50 years standing. Women generally live longer, thus there are many more widows than widowers. The loss of a partner can shatter a woman's life, especially if she has little or no emotional support from family and friends (see The Great Transition below). Indeed, studies have shown that those who have remained single all their lives generally feel more satisfied in late adulthood than widows or widowers of the same age.

However, the reward for grandparents is in watching their grandchildren (or even great-grandchildren) growing up. This is a source of joy for many people, especially since they do not have to deal with all the day-to-day problems and responsibilities of child-rearing.

Old age is a time for reflection and slowing down; a time to take stock of one's life, to look back over it and assess and evaluate how worthwhile and fulfilling it has been. It certainly helps if we can begin to accept that all life's experiences offer something of value – even the bad times. The lesson of winter, then, is to recognize how we have grown emotionally and spiritually as a result of life's ups and downs, triumphs and failures, calm and crisis.

Suggested Flower Essences

- *Angel's Trumpet* – for a balanced acceptance of the ageing process, especially physical deterioration and dying.
- *Chestnut Bud* – to enable one to learn the lessons of the life experience.
- *Gentian* – for pessimism and despair in the face of setbacks to physical health.
- *Holly* – for making peace in all relationships which need healing.
- *Honeysuckle* – for those who dwell too much in the past, paying little attention to the present.
- *Little Flannel Flower* – for those who need to learn to let go and have fun with their grandchildren; for connecting with the 'inner child'.
- *Pretty Face* – for those who cannot accept the ageing

process, being over-identified with their physical appearance.
- *Wild Rose* – for overcoming a tendency to apathy and resignation.
- *Willow* – for feelings of blame and bitterness about life.

The Great Transition

Preparing for our own death is a major development task in old age. Also it becomes increasingly likely that we will suffer the loss, through death, of loved ones, parents, husbands, siblings and friends.

While bereavement can be intensely painful – as can divorce or separation – sudden and untimely death, particularly of a child, can produce the greatest distress of all. But even when we know that someone close is about to die and will welcome an end of their suffering, when it actually happens it can be a greater shock than we had anticipated.

According to bereavement counsellors, it takes at least two years to fully finish grieving, and often longer than that. It is also generally agreed that there is a natural progression of feelings which must be worked through if a healthy adjustment to the loss is to be achieved. First there may be complete numbness or disbelief that the loved one has actually died. When it does register, the bereaved person may experience pangs of grief. Apathy, exhaustion and anger are also common, the last being closely related to self-blame and guilt. At this time it is important that we offer the grieving person our love and support, and be willing simply to listen, to hold their hand, to allow them to express their distress through tears of pain, anger and despair. After a while, as acceptance of the death emerges, the emotions die down. Eventually there is the realization that life must go on. Finally, acceptance is put into practice; the bereaved person learns to reorganize their life, a life in which the dead person has no place. However, pining and despair may reappear from time to time, perhaps triggered by an anniversary, birthday or, even more poignantly, by a whiff of the loved one's favourite perfume or aftershave.

It is vital for the bereaved person to express their grief, for grief cannot be suppressed. The feelings must go somewhere. Sometimes unexpressed grief may turn inwards, festering into a bitter and resentful outlook on life, or it may manifest as chronic physical tension. Moreover, those who are particularly hard hit by unexpressed grief, having little or no support from caring friends and relatives, are at high risk of developing mental and/or serious physical illness.

If the bereaved person does not have a close friend or family member who can fully support them in their grieving and the slow readjustment to life without their loved one, a professional person or someone skilled in bereavement support will be of enormous help to them.

Interestingly, studies have shown that those who experience a sensation of the presence of the departed loved one – and this can continue for years – are often better able to deal with their loss.

But what of the needs of the dying person? While many people die peacefully in their own beds, a great many more die in hospital. Hospitals are essentially geared towards cure and treatment, not comfort and palliative care. Hospital staff are generally overstretched and overworked. Through no fault of their own, they have neither the time nor the skills to offer real comfort and understanding to the dying person and their relatives. There is, therefore, an important place for specialist terminal care and this is provided by the relatively new hospice movement. Hospice skills are increasingly finding their way into the community – where support teams help families care for relatives at home. The first task of hospice care is to relieve physical pain and emotional distress. Only when the dying person has accepted the inevitability of death can they be truly free to live as fully as possible for all the time they have left. In fact, researchers have found that hospice patients with untreatable cancers who are aware of and can accept their condition, with the close support of their loved ones, tend to live for longer than might otherwise have been expected.

The final task of winter, whether it comes early or late, is to approach death consciously, calmly and without fear. This is the essence of what it is to be *truly* healed.

Suggested Flower Essences
Carefully chosen flower essences can bring comfort and support to both the dying person and to their family, friends and carers. The essences help us to express our feelings which, as we have already seen, is a vital part of the healing process. Moreover, many of the suggested remedies for the bereaved are also appropriate for those suffering as a result of divorce, the ending of a love affair or some other equally distressing trauma associated with loss. Although individual needs should always be taken into account, one or two of the following essences may prove helpful:

- *Agrimony* – for those who mask their own pain and suffering to please others.
- *Angel's Trumpet* – to enable an appropriate surrender to death.
- *Clematis* – for those who cannot face life without their loved one and choose to escape through excessive sleep.
- *Chamomile* – for sleeplessness, broken-heartedness and anger.

- *Holly* – for those who need to forgive others or to make peace with the world before death.
- *Mimulus* – for those who fear death.
- *Olive* – for carers who feel physically and emotionally exhausted.
- *Pine* – for those who punish themselves with guilt because they neglected the deceased when they were alive or for those who suffer from imagined guilt.
- *Rescue Remedy* (also *Star of Bethlehem*) – for those suffering from shock as a result of hearing of death or learning of an impending death.
- *Star of Bethlehem* – for those who suffer prolonged numbness as a result of shock and are therefore unable to properly grieve.
- *Sweet Chestnut* – for extreme mental anguish and grief, a sense of isolation, a feeling that one is cut off from God or from all other sources of help.
- *Wild Rose* – for those who are emotionally 'flat' or suffer from apathy as a result of bereavement.
- *Walnut* – the 'link breaker', for loved ones who may hold on too tightly, thus engendering guilt in the dying person who needs to be allowed to surrender to the dying process. The remedy will also help the dying person, especially if they find it difficult to surrender appropriately as a result of emotional pressure from loved ones.
- *Willow* – for those who feel bitter and resentful and blame others for their suffering.

So there is always a flower essence to help us cope with the stresses and strains of everyday life as well as the often difficult transitions of the female life-cycle. The remedies temper the March winds, yet blow softly on the heat of summer, thus easing our passage into autumn and winter. They help us truly to become a woman for all seasons.

Chapter Six

LEARNING TO LET GO

The key to good health and a sense of well-being lies in the realization that we need not be helpless victims of stress, which accounts for a great deal of illness. While our diet and lifestyle play a part, we need also to nurture our spiritual aspect, for we are more than a mind and a body. The spiritual aspect is tied up with our relationship with ourselves, with other people, and with our own sense of purpose and meaning. Without purpose we become depressed or apathetic; life then appears bleak and meaningless. Even when we do not follow a conscious spiritual path in terms of a religious faith, we may in fact be realizing our purpose in some other way. It could be through music or some other art form, no matter how humble, or simply through our work, family, relationships, or through a love of animals or nature – or more actively perhaps by working towards the realization of a humanitarian or Green ideal.

Stress Survival

Prolonged stress, whether it be the result of living in the fast track or through excessive monotony, can pave the way towards illness. So it is important to discover an enjoyable way of letting go and of enhancing our daily lives. The more we can do to help ourselves in this way, the more profound the effect of the flower essences. As well as nurturing our everyday needs, the essences will broaden our view, thus enabling us to realize our full potential. Indeed, this is the sole purpose of flower therapy as envisioned by Bach.

Before we go any further, every busy parent or carer looking after babies, young children, or perhaps an elderly parent or sick spouse, is certain to exclaim, 'But I haven't got time to sit down and relax!' However, it is essential that you do snatch some time to yourself each day – even as little as 15 minutes of peace and quiet will have a positive effect on your long-term health and well-being. Perhaps you could enlist the help of family and friends to build a supporting network, thus enabling you to share the responsibility with other parents or carers for minding the children or sitting with the dependent person. This will provide you, and your equally stressed friends, with the opportunity to leave the home environment, take some exercise and to do something you really enjoy doing.

Nature Attunement

Nature in her myriad forms is perhaps the most potent 'de-stressor' of all – a simple fact so often overlooked by many experts in the field of 'stress management'. She offers tranquillity to the frenzied and raises the spirits of the downhearted. All that she asks in return is a little of our time and attention. If you can only occasionally leave the city in order to visit the countryside, sea or mountains, do not despair: even the local park can be a source of healing. Breathe in the scents of flowers, trees and grasses; listen to the birds; feel the rough bark of a tree; walk on the soft earth;

embrace the elements. Do not be afraid of the wind or the rain, snow or frost. Wrap up warmly so that you need not hunch up against the cold, thus creating further tension. Let go – and enjoy!

If you are taking one of the tree remedies, such as *Oak*, *Hornbeam* or *Red Chestnut*, try to find the appropriate tree with which to attune. Breathe slowly and deeply and allow yourself to enjoy the presence of the tree; experience the different textures and scents of the bark and leaves, blossom or fruit. Silent contemplation of the tree's beauty and presence, even when not in leaf, can be a healing experience. Incidentally, if it is a very windy day, see if you can find a young tree, no more than 10 to 15 years old, with thin bark and in full leaf. Place your ear against the trunk and you will hear the sap rising up from the roots, compensating for the accelerated loss of moisture through the leaves – a delightful gurgling sound!

You can also attune to any other flower essence plant such as the powerful *Sunflower*, fragrant *Honeysuckle* or vibrant *Mimulus*. Much of the joy of this exercise is in the seeking (or growing) of the healing flowers.

Silent contemplation of moving water is another beautiful attunement. Close your eyes and listen to the falling rain, the music of a flowing river or waterfall, or the waves of the sea. If you live far from any natural source of moving water, an ornamental fountain in a park or garden can be of equal value.

For the physically able, what better way to commune with nature than to spend some time in the wilderness? There is something special about climbing a mountain, especially for the first time, or camping by the edge of a forest by a running stream, or walking on the remote high cliffs in summertime

– the wind and salt spray in your hair, the scent of wild flowers on the breeze, the springy turf underfoot, and the air resonating with the symphony of seabirds and crashing waves . . . There is something special indeed, something Otherworldly yet profoundly real about coming close to the Earth.

Deep Breathing

As breathing can be either voluntary or involuntary (at least up to a point), it can form a bridge between the conscious and the unconscious. By influencing our breathing, we can change our energy levels and our mood. To illustrate this, start to breathe shallowly, pant in and out very quickly for about half a minute. At the end of this time you will feel decidedly anxious – your heart will be pounding and you may even be experiencing fear. As an antidote, take three or four long, deep breaths from the abdomen and exhale slowly. You will find your mind and body sinking into a state of calm.

Many of us are shallow breathers (especially if we are under stress); we use only the upper part of our lungs, which means that toxic residues are not completely removed. As a result, the blood is deprived of much of the oxygen it needs to feed the body tissues, so we may end up feeling listless or suffering vagueness of thought. At the same time, the oxygen deficit hinders the assimilation of nutrients from the food we eat.

THE COMPLETE BREATH

One of the easiest ways to begin learning to breathe fully is to practise the yoga 'complete breath'. This exercise is also very beneficial to those suffering from respiratory ailments such as asthma, hay fever and bronchitis.

1. Ensure that your breathing is not constricted by tight clothing, and remove your shoes.
2. Lie on a rug on the floor (or on the ground if outside, perhaps in a garden), or alternatively on a firm bed, with your arms at your sides, several centimetres away from your body, palms facing down.
3. Close your eyes and begin to inhale very slowly through your nose . . .
4. Expand your abdomen slightly, then pull the air up into the rib-cage and then your chest. Your abdomen will be automatically drawn in as the ribs move out and the chest expands. Hold for a few seconds . . .
5. Now begin to breathe out slowly through your nose in a smooth continuous flow until the abdomen is drawn in and the rib-cage and chest are relaxed. Hold for a few seconds before repeating two or three times . . .
6. Now breathe in slowly as before, but this time gradually raise your arms overhead in time with the inhalation until the backs of your hands touch the floor. Hold your breath for five to ten seconds (according to your own capacity) while you have a good stretch, from fingertips to toes . . .
7. Slowly breathe out as you bring your arms back down to your sides. Repeat two or three times.

This exercise can be performed whilst standing. To enhance the stretch as you raise your arms overhead on the in-breath, stand on tiptoes, your heels coming back down again as you breathe out.

Deep Relaxation

Here is a deep relaxation exercise which can be very useful. Before you begin, find a quiet, well-ventilated room with a pleasantly relaxed decor. Wear loose, comfortable clothing and take off your shoes. If you live in a noisy area, it may also be helpful to play a tape or record of gentle music, but keep the volume down very low as your senses will be especially acute. Most important, ensure that you will not be disturbed for at least 15 minutes.

1. Lie down on the floor or on a firm bed supported by pillows if desired – one under your head and another under your knees to support your lower back.

2. Close your eyes, take one or two deep breaths through your nose, then breathe out through the mouth with a sigh . . .

3. Now become aware of your feet. Inhale through the nose and tighten your feet by first pointing your toes and then flexing the feet towards your body.

4. Hold on to this tension for a slow count or five, then let your feet relax as you breathe out through the mouth with a deep sigh . . .

5. As you inhale, tense your calves as you count slowly to five . . .

6. Progress to your knees, then your thighs, buttocks, abdomen, chest, shoulders, hands, arms, neck, head and face. Tense each part as you hold the breath, then let it go as you breathe out with a sigh through the mouth, experiencing a wonderful sensation of release . . .

7. Take three deep breaths, inhaling from the abdomen, but without straining. Hold each breath for a few seconds, then slowly exhale through the nose . . .

8. Now become aware of your body and 'feel' around your body with your mind for any areas that may still be tense, and repeat the tightening and releasing of the muscles until you feel deeply relaxed and at peace . . .

9. When you feel ready (after at least five minutes of
   lying quietly and breathing normally), have a good
   stretch from fingertips to toes before slowly getting
   up.

This exercise is most beneficial if practised once or twice a
day on an empty stomach, or at least half-an-hour after
eating a light meal or snack.

You may also find it helpful to take a dose of one of the
tranquillity essences first. *Chamomile* is an obvious choice, or
perhaps *Corn* if you are distressed or disorientated by the pace
of city life. *White Chestnut* is the remedy supreme for
enhancing relaxation and meditation, for it helps to still the
mind.

Movement

The following yoga sequence is known as the Sun Salutation
(*Surya Namaskar*) and is best described as a moving
meditation. It differs from other yoga postures or *asanas*
because each pose is held for no longer than two seconds,
one following on from the other in a continuous movement.
Yoga asanas are usually held for much longer than this.
Although at first sight the Sun Salutation looks complicated,
with practice you will soon be able to perform the sequence
as a flowing movement with synchronized breathing. If you
are reasonably supple, you should have little difficulty
bending into each position. If, however, you are quite stiff
or unused to this type of exercise, take it slowly, only bending
as far as your body will allow without causing pain. Sooner
rather than later, you will find your muscles and joints
loosening and allowing a free flow of movement. Repeat the
entire sequence two or three times. As your stamina and
flexibility increase, eventually you will enjoy performing 10

or even 12 rounds, three or four times a week.

If performed correctly, preferably first thing in the morning, the Sun Salutation flexes the whole body, improves lung capacity and increases strength and suppleness. At the same time, it brings about a feeling of joy and vitality – a wonderful way to start each day! The flower essence *Sunflower* taken just before performing the sequence will enhance the experience. This is a potent combination, especially during the winter months when you may be feeling below par as a result of light deprivation (see also page 86).

SUN SALUTATION
Take off your shoes and wear a comfortable track suit, leggings or, if it is warm enough, nothing at all, for it is vital not to restrict leg movement.

1. Stand erect with feet together and your hands in a prayer position held at the solar plexus (midriff); look straight ahead.
2. As you slowly breathe in, raise your arms overhead; bend back to arch your spine.
3. As you breathe out, bend forward as far as you can without strain. If possible, place the palms of hands on the floor beside your feet. Try not to bend your knees; tighten your abdomen and bring your head as close to your knees as possible.
4. Inhale; move your right leg in a backward step, knee touching the floor. The left knee should be between the hands.
5. Holding on to the breath, and without shifting the right leg, raise the knee off the floor, then move the left leg in a backward step to meet the right foot; look straight ahead.
6. Exhale, bend knees to touch the floor without

shifting your palms. Lower your body so that
forehead and chest come into contact with the
floor.

7. Inhale, bend forwards with arms straight, palms
   firmly on the floor.

8. Exhale, arch your back in a cat's stretch, head
   down between your arms. Do not strain, keep
   your head limp.

9. Inhale, bring the right leg forward alongside the
   palms. The left foot and knee should touch the
   floor.

10. Exhale, bend forward until your hands are in line
    with your feet; tighten your abdomen and bring
    your head as close as possible to your unbent
    knees.

11. Inhale and raise your arms overhead; bend back
    to arch your spine.

12. As you exhale, lower your arms to your sides.

Important: When repeating the posture (step 9) do remember to reverse the position of the legs.

Once you have completed a few rounds of the Sun Salutation (with half a minute's rest between each cycle), lie down on a firm surface (preferably a carpeted floor covered with a blanket) and allow yourself to completely let go. Lie there for at least five minutes, allowing your breathing and pulse rate to return to normal. When you are ready, slowly get up.

A Last Word

Flower therapy is not about fighting our emotional disturbances, which creates even more tension and conflict – just as tensing up against physical pain succeeds in causing greater discomfort. Rather, the flower essences enable us to express our emotions fully, thus helping to free any pent-up anger, fear or grief which may be gnawing away at our soul. Yet at the same time, the remedies enable us to observe our distress from a higher, more objective level of awareness. As the philosophers of ancient China would say: 'Distress is just like a restless horse, let it loose in a large meadow and it will eventually become calm and begin to graze.'

It may at first seem like masochism, but by acknowledging and accepting our negative emotions for what they are – a chance for us to learn and grow – we may pass through the darkness of pain to the sunlight of joy. Therefore, enter fully into the negativity for a while. If you are angry or jealous (*Holly*), scream and shout, beat the hell out of a cushion, or go to a Greek restaurant and smash a few plates! If you are depressed, but cannot cry (*Mustard*), read a sad novel, listen to melancholic music, indulge in nostalgia – anything to encourage the tears. The flower essences will then be free to transmute the distress into inner strength and renewed hope for the future. It helps to have a caring friend or loved one to hold your hand when the going gets tough. However, if you really cannot let go and the wounds continue to fester, especially if the distress is deep rooted or has lingered for a number of years, professional counselling or psychotherapy may be the answer. A caring therapist will help you to work through the feelings in a safe environment.

As well as learning to express emotion, it is important to find time for a few moments of silence each day (as advocated earlier). In so doing, you will learn to connect with a source of self-healing which resonates in harmony with the vibrations of the flower essences. After a while, you will begin to find that you are reacting less self-destructively to the pressures of life, becoming more resourceful in the face of adversity. It is a fact that the bodymind can either trap or liberate the spiritual aspect of self. The condition of spiritual imprisonment or freedom depends on many interrelated factors, but especially on how we think. Although we cannot always change our outer situation, with the help of the gentle flower essences, we can change our attitude to it, which makes all the difference in the world:

> *Two women look out through prison bars,*
> *The one sees mud, the other stars . . .*

BIBLIOGRAPHY

Bach, E., *Heal Thyself* (C. W. Daniel, 1931).

Barnard, J. and M., *The Healing Herbs of Edward Bach* (The Flower Remedy Programme, 1988).

Chopra, D., *Quantum Healing* (Bantam Books, 1992).

Collings, J., *Life Forces* (New English Library, 1991).

Dethlefsen, T. and Dahlke, R., *The Healing Power of Illness* (Element Books, 1991).

Greer, G., *The Change* (Hamish Hamilton, 1991).

Gross, R., *Psychology* (Hodder and Stoughton, 1990).

Hall, J., *The Wise Woman* (Element Books, 1992).

Hall, N., *The Moon and the Virgin* (The Women's Press, 1980).

Hayman, S., *Living with a Teenager* (Piatkus, 1988).

Holbeche, S., *The Power of Gems and Crystals* (Piatkus, 1989).

Howard J. and Ramsell J., *The Original Writings of Edward Bach* (C. W. Daniel, 1990).

Kaminski P. and Katz R., *Flower Essence Repertory* (The Flower Essence Society, 1992).

Kaplan-Williams, S., *The Elements of Dreamwork* (Element Books, 1990).

Kirsta, A., *The Book of Stress Survival* (Guild Publishing, 1991).

Macrae, J., *Therapeutic Touch* (Arkana, 1987).

Markham, U., *Women under Pressure* (Element Books, 1990).

Melville, A., *Natural Hormone Health* (Thorsons, 1990).

Ryerson, K., *Flower Essences and Vibrational Healing* (The Brotherhood of Life, 1987).

Scott, J., *Natural Medicine for Children* (Unwin and Hyman, 1991).

Shapiro, D., *The Bodymind Workbook* (Element Books, 1990).

Storch, M., *Painless Periods* (Arlington Books, 1982).

Vlamis, G., *Flowers to the Rescue* (Thorsons, 1986).

Westlake, A., *The Pattern of Health* (Element Books, 1985).

White, I., *Bush Flower Essences* (Bantam, 1991).

Wildwood, C., *Flower Remedies* (Element Books, 1992).

Winn, D., *The Hospice Way* (Optima, 1987).

Wolf, N., *The Beauty Myth* (Vintage, 1991).

SUGGESTED READING

Barnard, J. and M., *The Healing Herbs of Edward Bach* (The Flower Remedy Programme, 1988).

Hall, J., *The Wise Woman* (Element Books, 1992).

Howard J. and Ramsell J., *The Original Writings of Edward Bach* (C. W. Daniel, 1989).

Kaminski P. and Katz R., *Flower Essence Repertory* (The Flower Essence Society (California), 1992).

Melville, A., *Natural Hormone Health* (Thorsons, 1990).

Weeks, N., *The Medical Discoveries of Edward Bach, Physician* (C. W. Daniel, 1989).

White, I., *Bush Flower Remedies* (Bantam, 1991).

Wildwood, C., *Flower Remedies* (Element Books, 1992).

Winn, D., *The Hospice Way* (Optima, 1987).

Wolf, N., *The Beauty Myth* (Vintage, 1990).

USEFUL ADDRESSES

UK

Suppliers of the Bach Flower Remedies, also books and leaflets on the subject:

The Bach Centre,
Mount Vernon,
Sotwell,
Wallingford,
Oxfordshire,
OX10 OPZ
Tel: 0491 39489/34678

The Flower Remedy Programme,
PO Box 65,
Hereford,
HR2 OUW
  Though not connected with the Bach Centre, the above organization prepares flower remedies from the same plant species as advocated by Dr Bach.

To obtain the Californian essences, Australian Bush remedies and books on the subject, contact:

Phoenix By Mail
The Park,
Findhorn,
Morayshire,
Scotland,
IV36 022
Tel: 0309 691074

For courses in flower therapy, contact:

Clare Harvey,
The Shen Tao Foundation,
c/o Middle Piccadilly Natural Healing Centre,
Holwell,
Sherborne,
Dorset,
DT9 5LW
Tel: 0963 23468

If you suffer from seasonal affective disorder (SAD), as discussed in Chapter 5, and would like to obtain an anti-SAD light-box and/or full-spectrum lightbulbs, contact:

Full Spectrum Lighting Ltd,
Unit 1,
Riverside Business Centre,
Victoria Street,
High Wycombe,
Buckinghamshire,
HP11 2LT
Tel: 0495 448727

USA

To obtain the Californian
essences, books and other
literature on the subject, and to
find out about courses in flower
therapy, contact:

The Flower Essence Society,
PO Box 459,
Nevada City,
CA 959
Tel: 916 265 9163 or 800 548
0075

AUSTRALIA

To obtain the Bush essences,
books and other literature on the
subject, and to find out about
courses in flower therapy,
contact:

The Australian Flower Remedy
Society,
PO Box 531,
Spit Junction,
New South Wales 2088

INDEX

Numbers in *italic* refer to flower essence profiles.